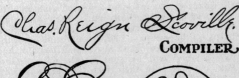

Preface

THE SINGING of hymns, and sacred songs has ever been one of the holiest and mightiest forces for the Kingdom of God, and the salvation of humanity. The infant and the aged, the conquering hero, the dying saint, and the dying soldier, all alike lean heavily upon the power of song. The Hebrews celebrated the discovery of a spring, the shadow of a rock in a weary land, and the gathering of the harvest, with song. And only when in hopeless captivity did they hang their harps on the willows. The angels sang over the manger, and the songs of Moses and the Lamb, and "a new song" will be sung in the City of God. Paul and Silas with their feet fast in the stocks, incarcerated in a foreign jail, at midnight, prayed and sang praises unto God. The armies of our Lord, as well as the armies of our lands have been marvelously inspired by the tremendous influence of song.

CHRISTIAN GOSPEL HYMNS is exactly what the title indicates, the Gospel in hymns for all Christians in all lands. We have culled the entire hymnology of the church, and have placed together here the very best of all the great hymns that they might beget reverence, devotion and consecration, in sacred worship. We have also secured the very cream of all the great new songs and choruses, that they might awaken life, and beget self-sacrifice, activity, and zeal *in all the organizations* carrying on the great work of the church.

Asking the Father's blessing that these songs may everywhere assist to exalt Christ, and save men, we are,

Yours in Jesus, for His glory,

CHAS. REIGN SCOVILLE.

No. 1. How Firm a Foundation.

George Keith.   Unknown.

1. How firm a foun-da-tion, ye saints of the Lord, Is laid for your faith in His
2. "Fear not I am with thee, O be not dis-mayed, For I am thy God, I will
3. "When thro' the deep waters I call thee to go, The riv-ers of sor-row shall
4. "When thro' fier-y tri-als thy path-way shall lie, My grace all suf-fi-cient shall

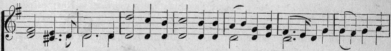

ex-cel-lent word! What more can He say than to you He hath said, To you, who for
still give thee aid; I'll strengthen thee, help thee, and cause thee to stand, Up-held by my
not o-ver-flow, For I will be with thee thy tri-als to bless, And sanc-ti-fy
be thy sup-ply, The flames shall not hurt thee; I on-ly de-sign Thy dross to con-

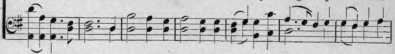

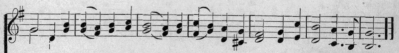

ref-uge to Je-sus have fled? To you who for ref-uge to Je-sus have fled.
gracious, om-nip-o-tent hand, Up-held by my gracious, om-nip-o-tent hand."
to thee thy deep-est dis-tress, And sanc-ti-fy to thee thy deepest distress."
sume, and thy gold to re-fine, Thy dross to consume, and thy gold to re-fine."

No. 2.

What Will It Be?

C. H. G.

Chas. H. Gabriel.

1. If to-day, a-mid the storms of life that wild-ly beat a-round us,
2. If His love so free-ly shed a-broad can fill our hearts with glo-ry,
3. If our faith in Him can fill our hearts with joy to o-ver-flow-ing,
4. If when those we love are tak-en from us we can still a-dore Him,

We the rain-bow of our bless-ed Lord can see, And re-joice to hear Him
If the sweet-est song of earth is: "Come to Me;" If such bless-ing it af-
And the Lord, un-seen, to us so dear can be; If we love Him while in
And to Him in that dark hour for com-fort flee; As we clasp their hands on

call-ing, as when first the Shepherd found us, When we stand in His presence,
fords us just to tell the pre-cious sto-ry, When we stand in His presence,
tears and pain for har-vest we are sow-ing, When we stand in His presence,
yon-der shore, to cast our crowns be-fore Him, And we stand in His presence,

D. S.—*As we stand in His pres-ence,*

FINE. CHORUS.

what will it be? What will it be? oh, what will it be? With the Lord to

what will it be?

D. S.

reign thro' all e-ter-ni-ty! On that bliss-ful shore, Sav'd for-ev-er-more,

No. 3. Do You Love Me More than These?

COPYRIGHT, 1909, BY CHAS. H. GABRIEL.
OWNED BY CHAS. REIGN SCOVILLE.

Jessie H. Brown.   Fred A. Fillmore.

1. When we fol-low earth-ly splen-dor, Seek-ing on-ly sel-fish ease;
2. When the crowns of hu-man glo-ry We, in blind-ness, try to seize;
3. Leaving home, and friends, and country, O-ver land and o-ver seas;

1. When we fol - low earthly splendor, Seeking on - ly selfish ease,

Bless-ed Lord, we hear Thee say-ing, "Do you love Me more than these?"
We can catch the ten-der ques-tion:—"Do you love Me more than these?"
We would follow when Thou call-est:—"Do you love Me more than these?"

Blessed Lord, we hear Thee saying, "Do you love Me more than these?"

CHORUS.

More than these, more than these, Do you love me more than these?

More than these, more than these, Do you love me more than these?

More, more than these, more, more than these,

Land of the Unsetting Sun.

W. C. Martin.   Chas. H. Gabriel.

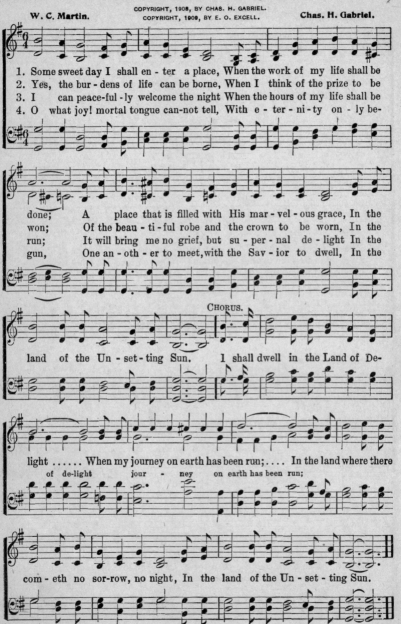

1. Some sweet day I shall en - ter a place, When the work of my life shall be
2. Yes, the bur - dens of life can be borne, When I think of the prize to be
3. I can peace - ful - ly welcome the night When the hours of my life shall be
4. O what joy! mortal tongue can-not tell, With e - ter - ni - ty on - ly be-

done;   A   place that is filled with His mar - vel - ous grace, In the
won;   Of the beau - ti - ful robe and the crown to be worn, In the
run;   It will bring me no grief, but su - per - nal de - light In the
gun,   One an - oth - er to meet, with the Sav - ior to dwell, In the

CHORUS.

land of the Un - set - ting Sun.   I shall dwell in the Land of De-

light ...... When my journey on earth has been run; .... In the land where there
of de - light   jour - ney   on earth has been run;

com - eth no sor - row, no night, In the land of the Un - set - ting Sun.

No. 5. The Great Change.

Chas. Reign Scoville.

De Loss Smith.

1. Since I'm in Christ and par-doned from sin, O what a world is
2. Fath-om-less love of e-ter-nal length, Weak-ness has changed to
3. Things I once loved are things I now hate, Since I have en-tered
4. That which was gain I count now but loss, What seemed pure gold I

this I'm now in! All things are changed by power di-vine, For I love
won-der-ful strength, All things are changed in "All mine are Thine," For I love
thro' the "Straight Gate." Toil all is pleas-ure, life is sub-lime, For I love
see now was dross: Tho' but a branch, I live in the Vine, For I love

CHORUS.

Christ and know He is mine. O what a change, O what a change, .
O what a change, _O what a change,_

Since thro' His blood . . . I'm saved by His grace; . . . And as He leads, . .
Since thro' His blood _by His grace;_ _And as He leads,_

still I shall change, Un-til I see . . . . . His face. . . . . .
still I shall change, _Un-til I see_ _beau-ti-ful face._

Help Somebody To-day.

Mrs. Frank A. Breck.

Chas. H. Gabriel.

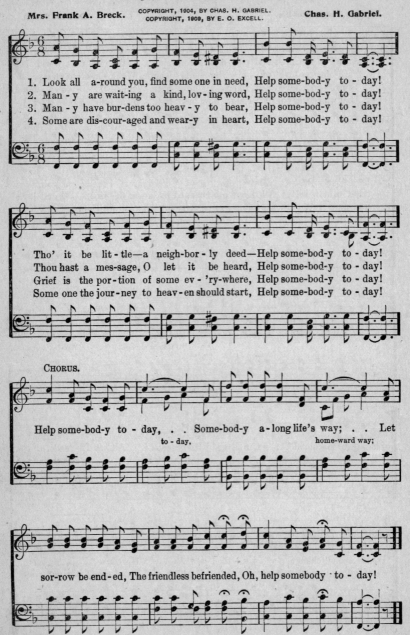

1. Look all a-round you, find some one in need, Help some-bod-y to - day!
2. Man - y are wait-ing a kind, lov-ing word, Help some-bod-y to - day!
3. Man - y have bur-dens too heav - y to bear, Help some-bod-y to - day!
4. Some are dis-cour-aged and wear-y in heart, Help some-bod-y to - day!

Tho' it be lit - tle—a neigh-bor - ly deed—Help some-bod-y to - day!
Thou hast a mes-sage, O let it be heard, Help some-bod-y to - day!
Grief is the por - tion of some ev - 'ry-where, Help some-bod-y to - day!
Some one the jour-ney to heav - en should start, Help some-bod-y to - day!

CHORUS.

Help some-bod-y to - day, . . Some-bod-y a - long life's way; . . Let
to - day,   home-ward way;

sor-row be end - ed, The friendless befriended, Oh, help somebody to - day!

No. 7. What Will You Do with Jesus?

Anon.   Harry W. Miller.

1. Je - sus is stand-ing in Pi - late's hall, Friendless, for - sak - en, be-
2. Je - sus is stand-ing on tri - al still, You can be false to Him
3. Will you e - vade Him as Pi - late tried, Or will you choose Him what
4. Will you like Pe - ter your Lord de - ny? Or will you scorn from His
5. "Je - sus, I give Thee my heart to - day; Je - sus, I'll fol - low Thee

trayed by all; Hark-en! what mean-eth the sud - den call?
if you will; You can be 'faith - ful thro' good or ill,
e'er be - tide? Vain - ly you strug-gle from Him to hide,
foes to fly, Dar - ing for Je - sus to live or die?
all the way, Glad - ly o - bey - ing Thee;" will you say;

CHORUS.

What will you do with Je - sus?
What will you do with Je - sus?
What will you do with Je - sus? What will you do with Je - sus? Neutral you
What will you do with Je - sus?
"This will I do with Je - sus?

can not be; Some day your heart will be ask-ing, What will He do with me?

No. 8. That's Enough for Me.

W. C. Martin.   Chas. H. Gabriel.

1. I do not ful-ly com-pre-hend The mer-cy shown to me;
2. So dark it was be-fore He came, And set my soul a-glow;
3. I do not know how it was done, How He has made me whole;
4. I do not ask to know the way He did His work of grace,

I on-ly know a Gra-cious Friend Has bro't my blindness to an end,
He kin-dled there a sa-cred flame, And tho' I scarce-ly knew His name,
I on-ly know the night is gone And day e-ter-nal has be-gun
So long as He has sent the ray, By which my spir-it can sur-vey

And now, thro' Him, I see, And now, thro' Him, I see.
He loves me—this I know, He loves me—this I know.
With-in my cloud-ed soul, With-in my cloud-ed soul.
The beau-ty of His face, The beau-ty of His face.

CHORUS.

So blind was I, but now I see, And that's e-nough for me;

So blind was I, but now I see, And that's e-nough for me.

No. 9. Let Jesus Come Into Your Heart.

C. H. M.

Mrs. C. H. Morris.

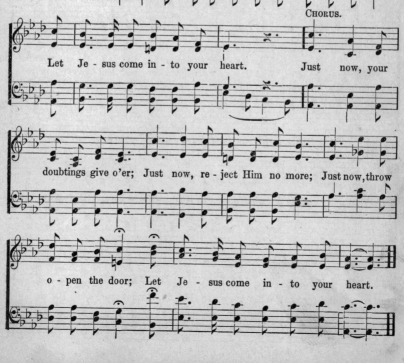

1. If you are tired of the load of your sin, Let Je-sus come in-to your heart; If you de-sire a new life to be-gin,
2. If 'tis for pu-ri-ty now that you sigh, Let Je-sus come in-to your heart; Fountains for cleans-ing are flow-ing near by,
3. If there's a tem-pest your voice can-not still, Let Je-sus come in-to your heart; If there's a void this world nev-er can fill,
4. If you would join the glad songs of the blest, Let Je-sus come in-to your heart; If you would en-ter the man-sions of rest,

Let Je-sus come in-to your heart.

CHORUS.

Just now, your doubtings give o'er; Just now, re-ject Him no more; Just now, throw o-pen the door; Let Je-sus come in-to your heart.

What More Can He Do.

Rachel Rivers.   Jno. R. Sweney.

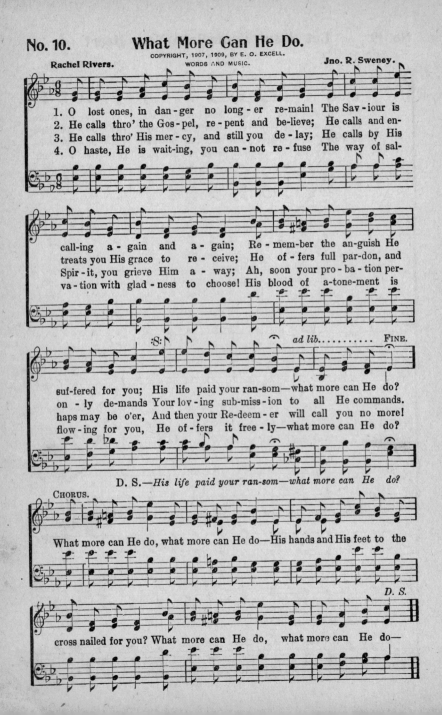

1. O lost ones, in dan-ger no long-er re-main! The Sav-iour is
2. He calls thro' the Gos-pel, re-pent and be-lieve; He calls and en-
3. He calls thro' His mer-cy, and still you de-lay; He calls by His
4. O haste, He is wait-ing, you can-not re-fuse The way of sal-

call-ing a-gain and a-gain; Re-mem-ber the an-guish He
treats you His grace to re-ceive; He of-fers full par-don, and
Spir-it, you grieve Him a-way; Ah, soon your pro-ba-tion per-
va-tion with glad-ness to choose! His blood of a-tone-ment is

ad lib.......... FINE.

suf-fered for you; His life paid your ran-som—what more can He do?
on-ly de-mands Your lov-ing sub-miss-ion to all He commands.
haps may be o'er, And then your Re-deem-er will call you no more!
flow-ing for you, He of-fers it free-ly—what more can He do?

D. S.—*His life paid your ran-som—what more can He do?*

CHORUS.

What more can He do, what more can He do—His hands and His feet to the

D. S.

cross nailed for you? What more can He do, what more can He do—

No. 11. There Will Be No Tears In Paradise.

Chas. Reign Scoville,

De Loss Smith.

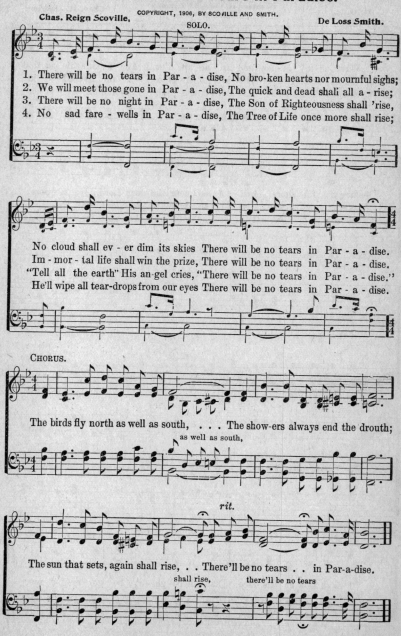

SOLO.

1. There will be no tears in Par - a - dise, No bro-ken hearts nor mournful sighs;
2. We will meet those gone in Par - a - dise, The quick and dead shall all a - rise;
3. There will be no night in Par - a - dise, The Son of Righteousness shall 'rise,
4. No sad fare - wells in Par - a - dise, The Tree of Life once more shall rise;

No cloud shall ev - er dim its skies There will be no tears in Par - a - dise.
Im - mor - tal life shall win the prize, There will be no tears in Par - a - dise.
"Tell all the earth" His an-gel cries, "There will be no tears in Par - a - dise."
He'll wipe all tear-drops from our eyes There will be no tears in Par - a - dise.

CHORUS.

The birds fly north as well as south, . . . The show-ers always end the drouth;
as well as south,

rit.

The sun that sets, again shall rise, . . There'll be no tears . . in Par-a-dise.
shall rise,   there'll be no tears

O That Will Be Glory.

C. H. G.

Chas. H. Gabriel.

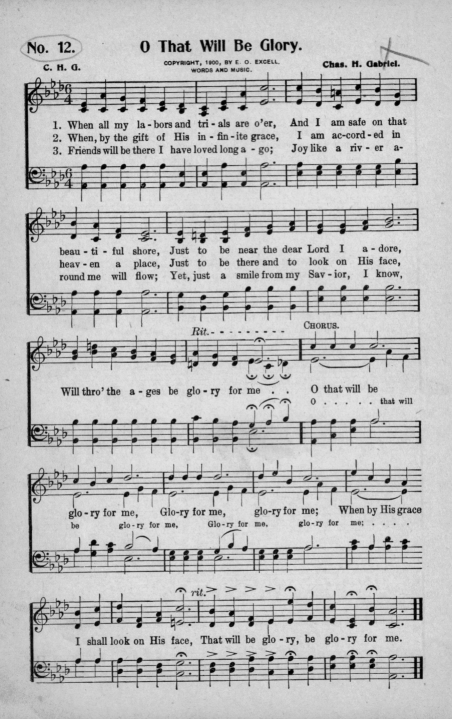

1. When all my la-bors and tri-als are o'er, And I am safe on that
2. When, by the gift of His in-fin-ite grace, I am ac-cord-ed in
3. Friends will be there I have loved long a - go; Joy like a riv - er a-

beau - ti - ful shore, Just to be near the dear Lord I a - dore,
heav - en a place, Just to be there and to look on His face,
round me will flow; Yet, just a smile from my Sav - ior, I know,

Rit. - - - - - - - - - CHORUS.

Will thro' the a - ges be glo - ry for me . . O that will be
O . . . . . that will

glo - ry for me, Glo-ry for me, glo - ry for me; When by His grace
be glo - ry for me, Glo-ry for me, glo-ry for me; . . . .

rit. > > > >

I shall look on His face, That will be glo - ry, be glo - ry for me.

No. 13. I Want to Live Closer to Jesus.

Jessie Brown Pounds.

COPYRIGHT, 1906, BY CHAS. H. GABRIEL.
E. O. EXCELL, OWNER.

Chas. H. Gabriel.

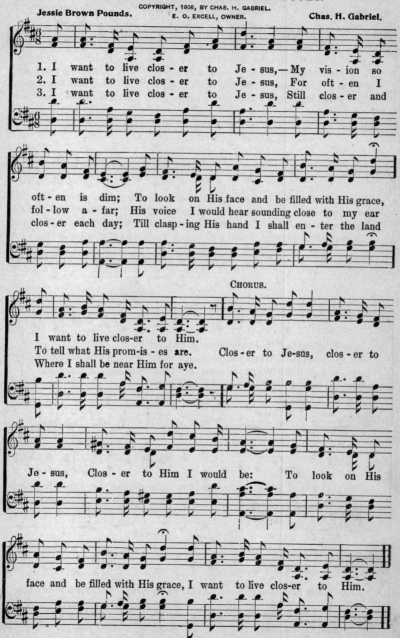

1. I want to live clos-er to Je-sus,—My vis-ion so
2. I want to live clos-er to Je-sus, For oft-en I
3. I want to live clos-er to Je-sus, Still clos-er and

oft-en is dim; To look on His face and be filled with His grace,
fol-low a-far; His voice I would hear sounding close to my ear
clos-er each day; Till clasp-ing His hand I shall en-ter the land

CHORUS.

I want to live clos-er to Him.
To tell what His prom-is-es are. Clos-er to Je-sus, clos-er to
Where I shall be near Him for aye.

Je-sus, Clos-er to Him I would be: To look on His

face and be filled with His grace, I want to live clos-er to Him.

No. 14.   Won't You Come Back Home?

James Rowe.   De Loss Smith.

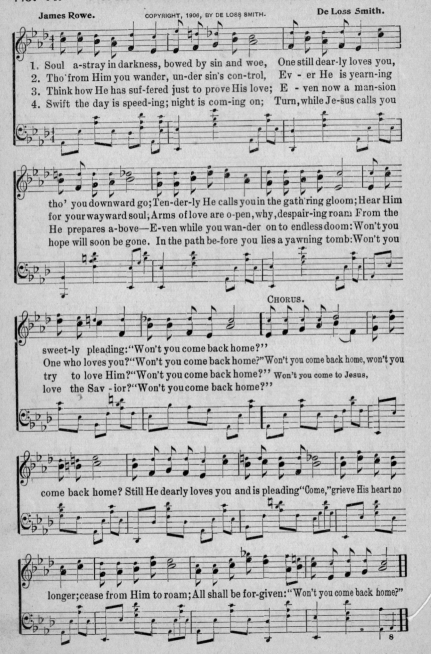

1. Soul a-stray in darkness, bowed by sin and woe, One still dear-ly loves you,
2. Tho' from Him you wander, un-der sin's con-trol, Ev - er He is yearn-ing
3. Think how He has suf-fered just to prove His love; E - ven now a man-sion
4. Swift the day is speed-ing; night is com-ing on; Turn, while Je-sus calls you

tho' you downward go; Ten-der-ly He calls you in the gath'ring gloom; Hear Him
for your wayward soul; Arms of love are o-pen, why, despair-ing roam From the
He prepares a-bove—E-ven while you wan-der on to endless doom: Won't you
hope will soon be gone. In the path be-fore you lies a yawning tomb: Won't you

Chorus.

sweet-ly pleading: "Won't you come back home?"
One who loves you? "Won't you come back home?" Won't you come back home, won't you
try to love Him? "Won't you come back home?" Won't you come to Jesus,
love the Sav - ior? "Won't you come back home?"

come back home? Still He dearly loves you and is pleading "Come," grieve His heart no

longer; cease from Him to roam; All shall be for-given: "Won't you come back home?"

8

No. 15.

Sweet Galilee.

WORDS AND MUSIC COPYRIGHT, 1903, BY E. O. EXCELL.
INTERNATIONAL COPYRIGHT SECURED.

Neal A. McAuley.   E. O. Excell.

1. I stood by the side of the mur-mur-ing sea, Sweet Gal-i-lee, sweet Gal-i-
2. I sailed in a ship on that bil - low-y sea, Sweet Gal-i-lee, sweet Gal-i-
3 I love to re - call the bright sil - ver-y sea, Sweet Gal-i-lee, sweet Gal-i-

lee; When the sun-shine its beau-ty re - vealed un - to me, Sweet Gal-i-lee,
lee; While the voice of the tem-pest was say - ing to me, Sweet Gal-i-lee,
lee; For its won - der-ful sto - ry is pre-cious to me, Sweet Gal-i-lee,

sweet Gal - i - lee; Then I thought of my Sav - ior who years long a-
sweet Gal - i - lee; Then I thought of the hearts who once tossed on the
sweet Gal - i - lee; As it tells of my Sav - ior who came from a-

go Came to tell the glad sto - ry, His love to be - stow, As He
wave, When they cried in their per - il to Him who could save; How the
bove, With the treas - ures of mer - cy and in - fi - nite love, Standing

stood by the side of that mur-mur-ing sea, Sweet Gal-i-lee, sweet Gal-i-lee.
Master spoke peace to that bil - low-y sea, Sweet Gal-i-lee, sweet Gal-i-lee.
there by the side of that sil - ver-y sea, Sweet Gal-i-lee, sweet Gal-i-lee.

No. 16. The Slighted Stranger.

C. H. G.

WORDS AND MUSIC COPYRIGHT, 1908, BY CHAS. H. GABRIEL.
E. O. EXCELL, OWNER

Chas. H. Gabriel.

1. A Stran-ger stands out-side the door, And longs thy guest to be;
2. From lone-ly, dark Geth-sem-a-ne, Thro' Pi-late's hall of shame,
3. Yet still He waits and calls to thee, Al-tho' ye scarce can hear

He knows thy name, for o'er and o'er He soft-ly calls to thee!
Up o-ver cru-el Cal-va-ry, To thee in love He came!
The plead-ing voice, so oft-en has It fall-en on thine ear:

His hands are pierced, His brow is torn, His face is sad, but sweet—
De-spised! re-ject-ed! cru-ci-fied! O love, O grace un-known,
O soul, a-rise and let Him in, Lest from the bolt-ed door

It is the Lord of Par-a-dise! A-rise, thy Sav-ior greet. . . .
That He should still re-mem-ber thee, And claim thee for His own! . . . .
In sor-row He should turn a-way, To call for thee no more. . . . .

CHORUS.

He was wounded for thy trans-gres-sions; He was bruis-ed for thy sin;

The Slighted Stranger.

Yet He stands at thy heart's door pleading, Why, O why not let Him in?

No. 17. Let the Lower Lights Be Burning.

P. P. B.

COPYRIGHT, 1905, BY THE JOHN CHURCH CO.
USED BY PER.

P. P. Bliss.

1. Bright-ly beams our Fa-ther's mer-cy From His light-house ev-er more,
2. Dark the night of sin has set-tled, Loud the an-gry bil-lows roar;
3. Trim your fee-ble lamp, my broth-er: Some poor sail-or tem-pest toss'd,

But to us He gives the keep-ing Of the lights a-long the shore.
Ea-ger eyes are watch-ing, long-ing, For the lights a-long the shore.
Try-ing now to make the har-bor, In the dark-ness may be lost.

CHORUS.

Let the low-er lights be burn-ing! Send a gleam a-cross the wave!

Some poor faint-ing struggling sea-man You may res-cue, you may save.

No. 18. Just When I Need Him Most.

Rev. Wm. Pool.

Chas. H. Gabriel.

1. Just when I need Him, Je-sus is near, Just when I fal - ter, just when I fear;
2. Just when I need Him, Je-sus is true, Nev-er for-sak - ing all the way thro';
3. Just when I need Him, Je-sus is strong, Bearing my bur-dens all the day long;
4. Just when I need Him, He is my all, An-swer-ing when up-on Him I call;

Read - y to help me, read - y to cheer, Just when I need Him most.
Giv - ing for bur - dens pleasures a - new, Just when I need Him most.
For all my sor - row giv - ing a song, Just when I need Him most.
Ten - der - ly watch-ing lest I should fall, Just when I need Him most.

CHORUS.

Just when I need Him most, Just when I need Him most;

Je - sus is near to com-fort and cheer, Just when I need Him most.

No. 19.   Jesus is All the World to Me.

W. L. T.   Will L. Thompson.

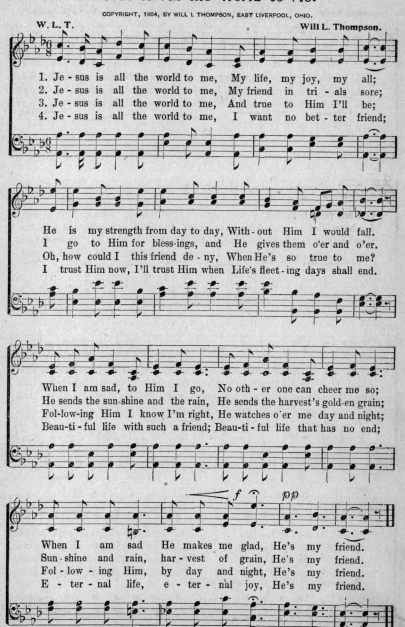

1. Je-sus is all the world to me, My life, my joy, my all;
2. Je-sus is all the world to me, My friend in tri-als sore;
3. Je-sus is all the world to me, And true to Him I'll be;
4. Je-sus is all the world to me, I want no bet-ter friend;

He is my strength from day to day, With-out Him I would fall.
I go to Him for bless-ings, and He gives them o'er and o'er.
Oh, how could I this friend de-ny, When He's so true to me?
I trust Him now, I'll trust Him when Life's fleet-ing days shall end.

When I am sad, to Him I go, No oth-er one can cheer me so;
He sends the sun-shine and the rain, He sends the harvest's gold-en grain;
Fol-low-ing Him I know I'm right, He watches o'er me day and night;
Beau-ti-ful life with such a friend; Beau-ti-ful life that has no end;

When I am sad He makes me glad, He's my friend.
Sun-shine and rain, har-vest of grain, He's my friend.
Fol-low-ing Him, by day and night, He's my friend.
E-ter-nal life, e-ter-nal joy, He's my friend.

No. 20. "Some Day" May be Too Late.

James Rowe. COPYRIGHT, 1908, BY DE LOSS SMITH. De Loss Smith.

1. "Some day," you say, when passing by souls bowed in grief and care, "When
2. "Some day," you say, when you behold some tott'ring slave to drink, "When
3. "Some day," you say, when Jesus pleads with tender voice and sweet, And
4. "Some day," you say, "I'll have more time my faith in Him to prove, And

fear and pride have fled a-way and I have time to spare, I'll la-bor
I have filled my store-house, I from du-ty shall not shrink; I'll fight the
shows to you His bleed-ing brow and side and hands and feet, "Some day, not
then I'll help my Lord to win the ob-ject of His love, That I may

rit.

for my Mas-ter, help these souls their ills to bear." "Some day" may be too late.
Liquor Traffic, snatch these brothers from the brink" "Some day" may be too late.
now, I'll heed His plea and seek the mer-cy seat." "Some day" may be too late.
win a shin-ing crown in par-a-dise a-bove." Some day" may be too late.

CHORUS.

"Some day" may be too late For death may shut the vineyard gate.
"Some day" may be too late For death may shut the vineyard gate.
"Some day" may be too late For death may call; oh, do not wait.
"Some day" may by too late For death may close the gold-en gate.

"Some day" may be too late

"Some Day" May be Too Late.

rit.

The time is now this ver-y hour, Some day may be to late.

No. 21.   I Love Him.

London Hymn Book.   USED BY PERMISSION.   S. C. Foster.

1. Gone from my heart the world with all its charm, Gone are my sins and
2. Once I was lost up-on the plains of sin, Ouce was a slave to
3. Once I was bound, but now I am set free; Once I was blind, but

all that would a-larm; Be-fore the cross my heart is bend-ing low, The
doubts and fears within, Once was a-fraid to meet an an-gry God, But
now the light I see; Once I was dead, but now in Christ I live, To

CHORUS.

precious blood of Je-sus cleanses white as snow.
now I'm cleansed from ev-'ry stain thro' Jesus' blood. I love Him, I love Him,
tell the world a-round the peace that He doth give.

Because He first loved me, And purchased my sal-va-tion on Cal-v'ry's tree.

No. 22. Growing Dearer Each Day.

C. H. G.   Chas. H. Gabriel.

1. How sweet is the love of my Savior! 'Tis bound-less and deep as the sea; And
2. I know He is ev-er be-side me! E-ter-ni-ty on-ly will prove The
3. Wher-ev-er He leads I will fol-low, Thro' sor-row, or shadow, or sun; And
4. Some day face to face I shall see Him, And oh, what a joy it will be To

best of it all, it is dai-ly Grow-ing sweet-er and sweeter to me.
height and the depth of His mercy, And the breadth of His in-fi-nite love.
tho' I be tried in the fur-nace, I can say, "Lord, Thy will be it done."
know that His love, now so precious, Will for-ev-er grow sweeter to me!

CHORUS.

Sweet-er and sweeter to me, ... Dear-er and
Sweet-er to me, grow-ing sweet-er to me. Dear-er each day,

dear-er each day; . . . Oh, won- - der-ful love of my
grow- ing dear-er each day; Oh, won-der-ful love, love of my

Sav-ior, Grow-ing dear- - er each step of my way!
Sav- ior, Grow-ing dear-er and dear-er each step of my way!

Coming King of Kings.

E. T. and F. H. Cassel.   Flora H. Cassel.

1. In Thine own word oh, bless-ed Lord Thy com - ing is for - told;
2. Oh, grant that we 'ere long may see, Thy com - ing in the sky,

We can not say how soon the day Will dawn and we be - hold
In splend-or bright and rai - ment white, With ang - els from on high;

The wondrous to - ken, of Thy word spok-en, Thy com-ing for Thine own,
Oh, speed the dawn-ing of that glad morn-ing, The com-ing of the King.

CHORUS.

O com - ing King of kings, My heart with rapt - ure sings,

I'll tell the sto - ry of Thy glo - ry, Com - ing King of kings.

No. 24. Nobody Told Me of Jesus.

Mrs. Frank A. Breck.   Chas. H. Gabriel.

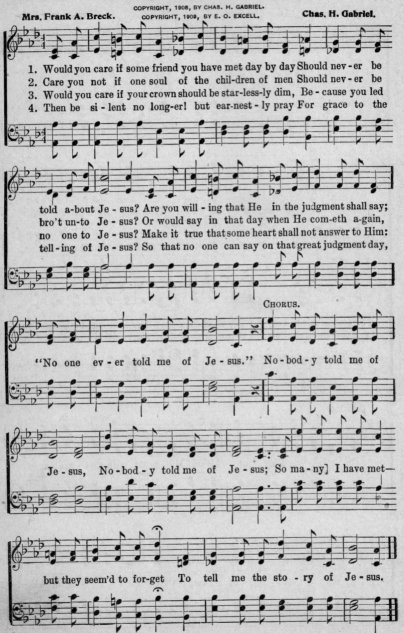

1. Would you care if some friend you have met day by day Should nev-er be
2. Care you not if one soul of the chil-dren of men Should nev-er be
3. Would you care if your crown should be star-less-ly dim, Be-cause you led
4. Then be si-lent no long-er! but ear-nest-ly pray For grace to the

told a-bout Je-sus? Are you will-ing that He in the judgment shall say;
bro't un-to Je-sus? Or would say in that day when He com-eth a-gain,
no one to Je-sus? Make it true that some heart shall not answer to Him:
tell-ing of Je-sus? So that no one can say on that great judgment day,

CHORUS.

"No one ev-er told me of Je-sus." No-bod-y told me of

Je-sus, No-bod-y told me of Je-sus; So ma-ny] I have met—

but they seem'd to for-get To tell me the sto-ry of Je-sus.

He is So Precious to Me.

1. So pre-cious is Je - sus, my Sav-ior, my King, His praise all the day long
2. He stood at my heart's door 'mid sunshine and rain, And pa-tient-ly wait - ed
3. I stand on the moun-tain of bless-ing at last, No cloud in the heav-ens
4. I praise Him be-cause He ap-point-ed a place Where, some day, thro' faith in

with rap - ture I sing; To Him in my weak-ness for strength I can cling,
an en-trance to gain; What shame that so long He en - treat - ed in vain,
a shad - ow to cast; His smile is up - on me, the val - ley is past,
His won - der - ful grace, I know I shall see Him—shall look on His face,

CHORUS. Faster.

For He is so pre-cious to me. For He is so pre-cious to
pre-cious to me, so pre-cious to me;
me, For He is so pre-cious to me; 'T is heaven be-

rit. - - -

low My Re-deem - er to know, For He is so pre-cious to me.

No. 26. His Love Can Never Fail.

COPYRIGHT, 1897, BY E. O. EXCELL.
WORDS AND MUSIC.

E. S. Hall.   E. O. Excell.

1. I do not ask to see the way My feet will have to tread;
2. And if my feet would go a-stray, They can-not, for I know
3. I will not fear, tho' dark-ness come A-broad o'er all the land,

But on - ly that my soul may feed Up - on the liv-ing bread.
That Je - sus guides my falt'ring steps, As joy - ful-ly I go.
If I may on - ly feel the touch Of His own lov-ing hand.

'Tis bet - ter far that I should walk By faith close to His side,—
And tho' I may not see His face, My faith is strong and clear,
And tho' I trem-ble when I think How weak I am, how frail,

I may not know the way I go, But oh, I know my Guide.
That in each hour of sore dis-tress My Sav - ior will be near.
My soul is sat - is - fied to know His love can nev - er fail.

D. S.—*My soul is sat - is - fied to know His love can nev - er fail.*

CHORUS.

His love .. can nev - er fail, His love .. can nev - er fail;
His love can nev - er fail.   His love can nev - er fail;

He is Able to Deliver Thee.

W. A. O.

COPYRIGHT, 1887, BY E. O. EXCELL.
WORDS AND MUSIC.

W. A. Ogden.

1. 'Tis the grand-est theme thro' the a-ges rung; 'Tis the grand-est
2. 'Tis the grand-est theme in the earth or main; 'Tis the grand-est
3. 'Tis the grand-est theme, let the ti-dings roll To the guilt-y

theme for a mor-tal tongue; 'Tis the grandest theme that the world e'er sung,
theme for a mor-tal strain; 'Tis the grandest theme, tell the world a-gain,
heart, to the sin-ful soul; Look to God in faith, He will make thee whole,

CHORUS.

"Our God is a-ble to de-liv-er thee." He is a - - - ble to de-
a-ble, He is a-ble

liv-er thee, He is a - - - ble to de-liv-er thee; Tho' by sin op-
a-ble, He is a-ble

prest, Go to Him for rest, "Our God is a-ble to de-liv-er thee."

No. 28.

Beyond the Bar.

T. M. Eastwood.

Fred. H. Byshe.

1. Be-yond the bar on yon-der shore, A-cross life's troubled sea, There
2. Be-yond the bar my King a-bides, A-mong His jew-els rare; And
3. Be-yond the bar there is no death, And sor-row reigns no more; There
4. Be-yond the bar we'll meet a-gain The friends we've missed so long; And

is a cit-y bright and fair   Pre-pared for me, pre-pared for me.
some day I shall dwell with Him,— My home is there, my home is there.
are no bruised and bleeding hearts On that blest shore, on that blest shore.
with them sing, for-ev-er-more, Un-end-ing song, un-end-ing song.

CHORUS.

I'll need no light   of sun or star,   When I my Sav-ior's face shall
Need no light of   sun or star,   When my Sav-ior's

see;   That will be light   e-nough for me,   Throughout a
face I see;   Light e-nough, e-   nough for me,

blest   e-ter-ni-ty,   Be-yond the bar, be-yond the bar.
Thro' a blest   e-   ter-ni-ty,

No. 31. The Way of the Cross Leads Home.

Jessie Brown Pounds.

Chas. H. Gabriel.

1. I must needs go home by the way of the cross, There's no oth-er
2. I must needs go on in the blood-sprinkled way, The path that the
3. Then I bid fare-well to the way of the world, To walk in it

way but this; I shall ne'er get sight of the Gates of Light,
Sav-ior trod, If I ev-er climb to the heights sub-lime,
nev-er more; For my Lord says "Come," and I seek my home,

CHORUS.

If the way of the cross I miss.
Where the soul is at home with God. The way of the cross leads
Where He waits at the o-pen door.

home, The way of the cross leads home; It is
leads home, leads home;

sweet to know, as I on-ward go, The way of the cross leads home.

Be Ye Also Ready.

Chas. Reign Scoville.   COPYRIGHT, 1906, BY SCOVILLE AND SMITH.   De Loss Smith.

1. I know not how soon Christ is com-ing a-gain; But He said, "Be ye
2. Of that day and hour, there is no man who knows, No, not e - ven the
3. If read-y to live, you are read-y to die, Or to en-ter the
4. The Mas-ter may tar-ry, but don't be deceived; Like the vir-gins no

read-y to go;" The clouds shall de-scend and the trumpet shall sound,
an - gels of light; The Fa-ther's own bo-som the se - cret con-ceals,
por - tals of light; At mid-night or noon, He will not come too soon,
oil for your light; There's no time to buy, when the Bridegroom draws nigh,

CHORUS.

O Broth-er, be read-y to go.
So, Broth-er, be read-y to - night. In an hour that you think not your
Then come to the Sav-ior to - night.
O Broth-er, be read-y to - night.

life here will end; In an hour that you think not, and so, Be ye chil-dren of

Be Ye Also Ready.

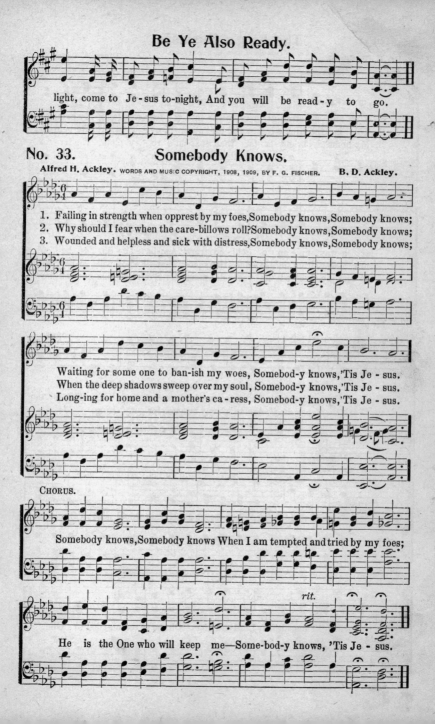

light, come to Je-sus to-night, And you will be read-y to go.

No. 33. Somebody Knows.

Alfred H. Ackley. WORDS AND MUSIC COPYRIGHT, 1908, 1909, BY F. G. FISCHER. B. D. Ackley.

1. Failing in strength when opprest by my foes, Somebody knows, Somebody knows;
2. Why should I fear when the care-billows roll? Somebody knows, Somebody knows;
3. Wounded and helpless and sick with distress, Somebody knows, Somebody knows;

Waiting for some one to ban-ish my woes, Somebod-y knows, 'Tis Je - sus.
When the deep shadows sweep over my soul, Somebod-y knows, 'Tis Je - sus.
Long-ing for home and a mother's ca - ress, Somebod-y knows, 'Tis Je - sus.

CHORUS.

Somebody knows, Somebody knows When I am tempted and tried by my foes;

rit.

He is the One who will keep me—Some-bod-y knows, 'Tis Je - sus.

No. 34. The King's Business.

Dr. E. T. Cassel.

Flora H. Cassel.

1. I am a stran-ger here, with-in a for-eign land; My home is
2. This is the King's command: that all men, ev-'ry-where, Re-pent and
3. My home is bright-er far than Shar-on's ro-sy plain, E-ter-nal

far a-way, up-on a gold-en strand; Am-bas-sa-dor to be of
turn a-way from sin's se-duc-tive snare; That all who will o-bey, with
life and joy thro'-out its vast do-main; My Sov'reign bids me tell how

CHORUS.

realms be-yond the sea, I'm here on business for my King.
Him shall reign for aye, And that's my business for my King. This is the
mor-tals there may dwell, And that's my business for my King.

mes-sage that I bring, A message angels fain would sing; "Oh, be ye

reconciled," Thus saith my Lord and King, "Oh, be ye rec-on-ciled to God."

Sunshine and Rain.

WORDS AND MUSIC COPYRIGHT, 1902, BY CHAS. H. GABRIEL.
E. O. EXCELL, OWNER.

C. H. G.

Chas. H. Gabriel.

1. Had we on - ly sun-shine all the year a-round, With-out the bless-ing
2. Had we not a sor - row or a cross to bear, For Him who bore the
3. Can we prize the sun-shine and de-plore the rain, Re - pin - ing when the

of re-fresh-ing rain,
bur-den of our sin,
days are dark and drear?

Would we scatter seed up - on the fal-low
Would we know the sweetness of His love and
Can we hope for pleasures, yet de-ny the

CHORUS.

ground, And hope to gather flow-ers, fruit and grain?
care, Or e - ven strive e - ter-nal joys to win? Sun-shine and rain re-
pain, Or share the joys of life with-out the tear?

freshing, reviving rain, Light of faith and love, Showers from above! Sunshine and

rain, to nourish the growing grain, Send us, Lord, the sunshine and the rain.

No. 36.   His Love is All I Need.

E. O. E.

E. O. Excell.

1. The love of Je-sus, who can tell, Tho' he may know it, oh, so well?
2. The love of Je-sus, oh, what bliss! To hear Him whis-per, I am His;
3. The love of Je-sus, oh, how sweet! To hide in such a safe re-treat;

The love that ev-'ry want sup-plies, The love that al-ways sat-is-fies;
Tho' I may fal-ter on the way, He will not let me go a-stray;
Tho' Sa-tan would my hopes de-stroy, My Sav-ior's love is still my joy;

rit.   CHORUS.

His love is all I need! So won-der-ful, His love to me,

More won-der-ful how could it be? My ev-'ry sin on Him was laid,

rit.

My ev-'ry debt by Him was paid; His love is all I need!

Higher Ground.

Rev. Johnson Oatman, Jr.   JOHN J. HOOD, OWNER.   Chas. H. Gabriel.

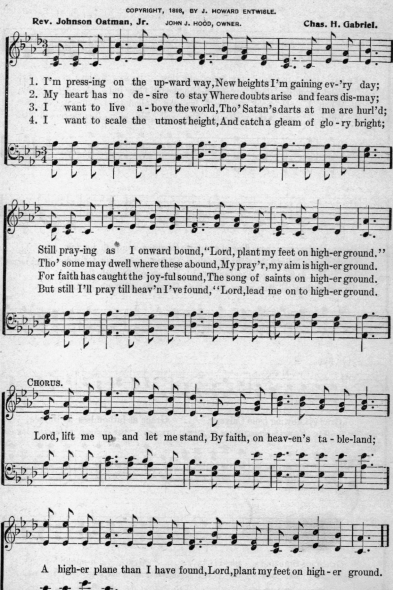

1. I'm press-ing on the up-ward way, New heights I'm gaining ev-'ry day;
2. My heart has no de-sire to stay Where doubts arise and fears dis-may;
3. I want to live a-bove the world, Tho' Satan's darts at me are hurl'd;
4. I want to scale the utmost height, And catch a gleam of glo-ry bright;

Still pray-ing as I onward bound, "Lord, plant my feet on high-er ground."
Tho' some may dwell where these abound, My pray'r, my aim is high-er ground.
For faith has caught the joy-ful sound, The song of saints on high-er ground.
But still I'll pray till heav'n I've found, "Lord, lead me on to high-er ground.

CHORUS.

Lord, lift me up and let me stand, By faith, on heav-en's ta-ble-land;

A high-er plane than I have found, Lord, plant my feet on high-er ground.

No. 38. Grace, Enough for Me.

E. O. E.

E. O. Excell.

1. In look-ing thro' my tears one day, I saw Mount Cal-va-ry;
2. While stand-ing there, my trem-bling heart, Once full of ag-o-ny,
3. When I be-held my ev-'ry sin Nailed to the cru-el tree,
4. When I am safe with-in the veil, My por-tion there will be,

cres.

Be-neath the cross there flowed a stream Of grace, e-nough for me.
Could scarce believe the sight I saw Of grace, e-nough for me. (enough for me.)
I felt a flood go thro' my soul Of grace, e-nough for me.
To sing thro' all the years to come Of grace, e-nough for me.

CHORUS.

Grace is flowing from Calvary, . . . Grace as fathomless as the sea, . .
Grace is flow-ing from Cal-va-ry for me, Grace as fath-om-less as the roll-ing sea,

Grace for time and e-ter-ni-ty, . . . Grace, e-nough for me.
Grace for time and e-ter-ni-ty, A-bun-dant grace I see, e-nough for me.

No. 39. Just for His Sake.

Mrs. S. M. I. Henry. M. H. Evans.

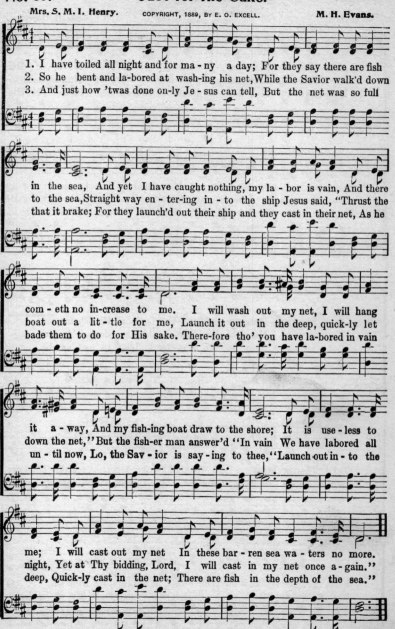

1. I have toiled all night and for ma - ny a day; For they say there are fish in the sea, And yet I have caught nothing, my la - bor is vain, And there com - eth no in-crease to me. I will wash out my net, I will hang it a - way, And my fish-ing boat draw to the shore; It is use - less to me; I will cast out my net In these bar - ren sea wa - ters no more.

2. So he bent and la-bored at wash-ing his net, While the Savior walk'd down to the sea, Straight way en - ter-ing in - to the ship Jesus said, "Thrust the boat out a lit - tle for me, Launch it out in the deep, quick-ly let down the net," But the fish-er man answer'd "In vain We have labored all night, Yet at Thy bidding, Lord, I will cast in my net once a - gain."

3. And just how 'twas done on-ly Je - sus can tell, But the net was so full that it brake; For they launch'd out their ship and they cast in their net, As he bade them to do for His sake. There-fore tho' you have la-bored in vain un - til now, Lo, the Sav - ior is say-ing to thee, "Launch out in - to the deep, Quick-ly cast in the net; There are fish in the depth of the sea."

No. 40. More Like the Master.

C. H. G.

Chas. H. Gabriel.

1. More like the Mas-ter I would ev-er be, More of His
2. More like the Mas-ter is my dai-ly pray'r, More strength to
3. More like the Mas-ter I would live and grow, More of His

meek-ness, more hu-mil-i-ty; More zeal to la-bor, more cour-age
car-ry cross-es I must bear; More earn-est ef-fort to bring His
love to oth-ers I would show; More self-de-ni-al, like His in

to be true, More con-se-cra-tion for work He bids me do.
king-dom in, More of His Spir-it, the wan-der-er to win.
Gal-i-lee, More like the Mas-ter I long to ev-er be.

CHORUS.

Take Thou my heart ...... I would be Thine a-lone; ..... Take Thou my
Take my heart, O take my heart, I would be Thine a-lone; Take my heart, O

heart .... and make it all Thine own; ... Purge me from sin, ... O
take my heart and make it all Thine own; Purge Thou me from ev-'ry sin, O

More Like the Master.

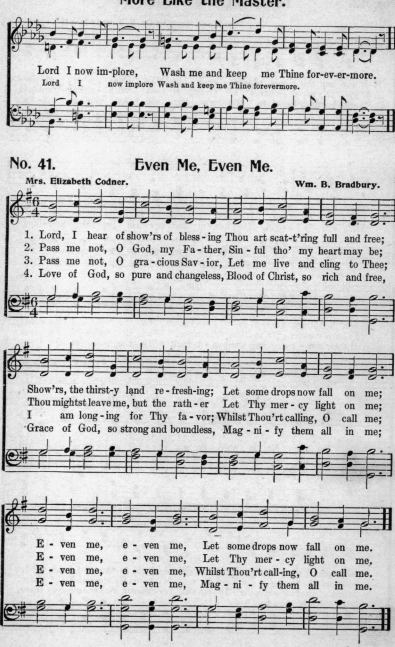

Lord I now im-plore,   Wash me and keep   me Thine for-ev-er-more.
Lord   I   now implore Wash and keep me Thine forevermore.

No. 41.   ## Even Me, Even Me.

Mrs. Elizabeth Codner.   Wm. B. Bradbury.

1. Lord, I hear of show'rs of bless-ing Thou art scat-t'ring full and free;
2. Pass me not, O God, my Fa-ther, Sin-ful tho' my heart may be;
3. Pass me not, O gra-cious Sav-ior, Let me live and cling to Thee;
4. Love of God, so pure and changeless, Blood of Christ, so rich and free,

Show'rs, the thirst-y land re-fresh-ing; Let some drops now fall on me;
Thou mightst leave me, but the rath-er Let Thy mer-cy light on me;
I am long-ing for Thy fa-vor; Whilst Thou'rt calling, O call me;
Grace of God, so strong and boundless, Mag-ni-fy them all in me;

E - ven me, e - ven me, Let some drops now fall on me.
E - ven me, e - ven me, Let Thy mer-cy light on me.
E - ven me, e - ven me, Whilst Thou'rt call-ing, O call me.
E - ven me, e - ven me, Mag-ni-fy them all in me.

No. 42.

Ye Have Done It Unto Me.

COPYRIGHT, 1906, BY SCOVILLE & SMITH.

Words and Music by Dr. E. T. and Flora H. Cassel.

1. Borne on the wings of a chill-ing blast, Came a cry of dis-
2. Once to my door came a strang-er old, With a hag-gard and
3. Hark! broth-er hark! to the cry for aid, As you go up-on

tress and of woe; I hastened my steps, I would hur-ry past,
pit-i-ful face, He cried, "Take me in from the paths of sin
life's dai-ly round, The hun-gry and per-ish-ing faint and fade

When the thought came to me I know 'Tis the voice of Je-sus
I have wander-ed in deep dis-grace." 'Twas the voice of Je-sus
And their sor-row and want a-bound. 'Tis the voice of Je-sus

call-ing me He is need-ing my suc-cor and care. I will
call-ing me He was need-ing my suc-cor and care. In the
call-ing thee He is need-ing my suc-cor and care. In the

help what I can, oh, my Lord for Thee And aid to the suf-f'ring bear.
form of the strang-er my Lord I see My home He shall sure-ly share.
forms of the low-ly your Sav-ior see, Your wealth with the need-y share.

Ye Have Done It Unto Me.

CHORUS.

"In as much as ye did it to one of these" He ten-der-ly said, "ye have done it to me; In as much as ye did it to one of these, ye have done it un-to me."

No. 43. Where He Leads Me.

E. W. Blandly.　　　　　　　　　　　　　　　　　　J. S. Norris.

1. I can hear my Sav-ior call-ing, I can hear my Sav-ior call-ing,
2. I'll go with Him thro' the gar-den, I'll go with Him thro' the gar-den,
3. I'll go with Him thro' the judgment, I'll go with Him thro' the judgment,
4. He will give me grace and glo-ry, He will give me grace and glo-ry,

D.C.—*Where He leads me I will fol-low, Where He leads me I will fol-low,*

ad lib.　　　　　　　　　　　　　　　　　　*D. C.*

I can hear my Sav-ior call-ing, "Take thy cross and follow, fol-low me."
I'll go with Him thro' the gar-den, I'll go with Him, with Him all the way.
I'll go with Him thro' the judgment, I'll go with Him, with Him all the way.
He will give me grace and glo-ry, And go with me, with me all the way.

Where He leads me I will fol-low, I'll go with Him, with Him all the way.

No. 44. Count Your Blessings.

COPYRIGHT, 1897, BY E. O. EXCELL.
WORDS AND MUSIC.

Rev. J. Oatman, Jr.   E. O. Excell.

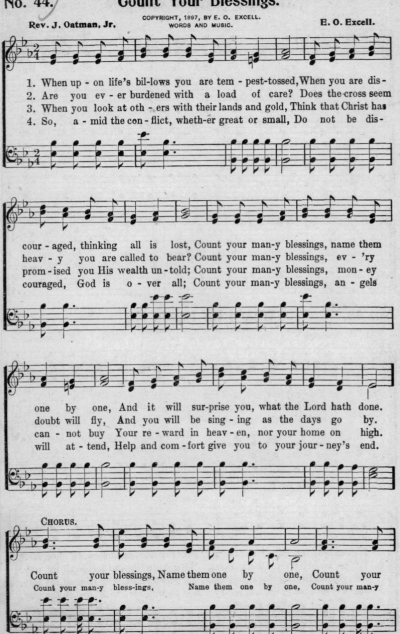

1. When up-on life's bil-lows you are tem-pest-tossed, When you are dis-
2. Are you ev-er burdened with a load of care? Does the cross seem
3. When you look at oth-ers with their lands and gold, Think that Christ has
4. So, a-mid the con-flict, wheth-er great or small, Do not be dis-

cour-aged, thinking all is lost, Count your man-y blessings, name them
heav-y you are called to bear? Count your man-y blessings, ev-'ry
prom-ised you His wealth un-told; Count your man-y blessings, mon-ey
couraged, God is o-ver all; Count your man-y blessings, an-gels

one by one, And it will sur-prise you, what the Lord hath done.
doubt will fly, And you will be sing-ing as the days go by.
can-not buy Your re-ward in heav-en, nor your home on high.
will at-tend, Help and com-fort give you to your jour-ney's end.

CHORUS.

Count your blessings, Name them one by one, Count your
Count your man-y bless-ings, Name them one by one, Count your man-y

Count Your Blessings.

bless - ings, See what God hath done; Count your blessings,
bless - ings, See what God hath done; Count your man - y bless-ings,

Name them one by one, Count your man-y blessings, See what God hath done.

No. 45. I am Trusting, Lord, in Thee.

Wm. McDonald.   USED BY PERMISSION.   **W. G. Fischer.**

1. I am com - ing to the cross; I am poor, and weak, and blind;
2. Long my heart has sighed for Thee, Long has e - vil reigned with - in;
3. Here I give my all to Thee, Friends, and time, and earth - ly store;

CHO.—*I am trust-ing, Lord, in Thee; Blest Lamb of Cal - va - ry;*

D. C. for Chorus.

I am count - ing all but dross, I shall full sal - va - tion find.
Je - sus sweet - ly speaks to me,— "I will cleanse you from all sin."
Soul and bod - y Thine to be, Whol - ly Thine for - ev - er - more.

Hum - bly at Thy cross I bow, Save me, Je - sus, save me now.

The Bells of Conscience.

Words and Music by J. M. Dungan.

1. The con-science of child-hood is speak-ing in whis-pers, Oh come to the Sav-ior and give Him your life, "Of such is the king-dom of heav-en," says Je-sus, So then seek Him ear-ly, and en-ter the strife.

2. The con-science of young men and maid-ens is call-ing, In earn-est ap-peals for the strength or your will, The work of your Mas-ter it needs all your ef-forts, To bear all life's bur-dens, and Christ's law ful-fill.

3. The con-science of man-hood is loud-ly ap-peal-ing, And say-ing, oh come in the noon-tide of day, The sands of your hour-glass are slow-ly re-ced-ing, So start for the king-dom and do not de-lay.

4. The con-science of old age is heav-i-ly la-den, With sins which thro' life have been heav-y to bear, But Je-sus is a-ble to roll off thy bur-den, To cleanse you from e-vil and hit ev-'ry care.

The Bells of Conscience.

CHORUS.

The bells of your conscience are ring-ing, The bells the bells, The bells of your conscience are ring-ing, Say-ing sin-ner, Oh, come home.

No. 47. We'll Work till Jesus Comes.

Elizabeth Mills. USED BY PERMISSION. **William Miller.**

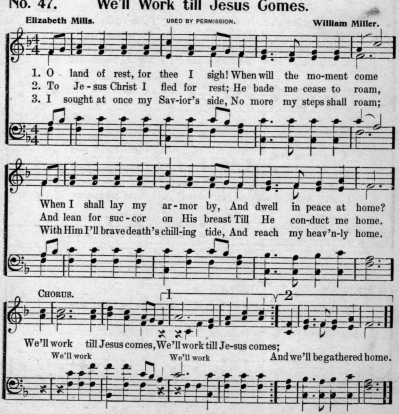

1. O land of rest, for thee I sigh! When will the mo-ment come
2. To Je-sus Christ I fled for rest; He bade me cease to roam,
3. I sought at once my Sav-ior's side, No more my steps shall roam;

When I shall lay my ar-mor by, And dwell in peace at home?
And lean for suc-cor on His breast Till He con-duct me home.
With Him I'll brave death's chill-ing tide, And reach my heav'n-ly home.

CHORUS.

We'll work till Jesus comes, We'll work till Je-sus comes;
We'll work We'll work And we'll be gathered home.

My Father Planned It All.

H. H. Pierson.

Chas. H. Gabriel.

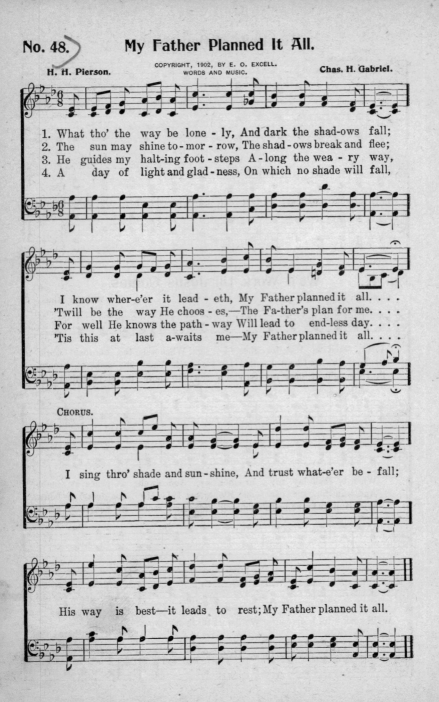

1. What tho' the way be lone - ly, And dark the shad-ows fall;
2. The sun may shine to - mor - row, The shad - ows break and flee;
3. He guides my halt-ing foot - steps A - long the wea - ry way,
4. A day of light and glad - ness, On which no shade will fall,

I know wher-e'er it lead - eth, My Father planned it all. . . .
'Twill be the way He choos - es,—The Fa-ther's plan for me. . . .
For well He knows the path - way Will lead to end-less day. . . .
'Tis this at last a-waits me—My Father planned it all. . . .

Chorus.

I sing thro' shade and sun - shine, And trust what-e'er be - fall;

His way is best—it leads to rest; My Father planned it all.

No. 49. Forward All.

T. E. Jones.   Arr. by O. S. Grinnell.

1. For-ward all, put on the gos-pel ar-mor, Read-y, stand, to fight for Christ the Lord; Take His shield and hel-met of sal-va-tion, On-ward trust-ing ev-er in His word.

2. On-ward, still ye val-iant hap-py sol-diers, Go with faith to con-quer ev-'ry sin; In the strength of Je-sus we will tri-umph, In His name the vic-t'ry we will win.

3. On-ward, still keep mov-ing ev-er on-ward, Till we reach fair Canaan's hap-py shore; There to dwell for-ev-er with our Cap-tain, And to sing His prais-es ev-er-more.

CHORUS.

On-ward ye sol-diers of Je-sus, On-ward, forward, march to-geth-er,

Hold a-loft His banner, Shout aloud ho-san-na Faith-ful-ly, follow your Leader,
Hold a-loft His ban-ner, sol-diers, Be ye faith-ful to your Lead-er,

And the vict'ry you shall win; follow your Leader, And the vict'ry you shall win.

No. 50.   Eternity.

F. A. S.   Frank A. Simpkins.

1. There is a   Cit - y, I am   told   Where all the
2. Me thinks I   hear   the heav'n-ly   song,   In hal - le-
3. Our loved ones   who   have gone be - fore,   Are beck-'ning
4. Some day my   bless - ed Lord will   call,   In tones that

streets are paved with gold;   A Home pre - pared   for you and
lu - jahs loud and long: Come float-ing o'er   the might-y
us   to that bright shore;   That we may from   our cares be
gen - tly rise and fall;   And He will say "Come home with

me, Where we may spend   e - ter - ni - ty.............   E - ter - ni-
sea,   A mes-sage from   e - ter - ni - ty.............   E - ter - ni-
free,   And sing thro' all   e - ter - ni - ty.............   E - ter - ni-
me,   To dwell in   blest   e - ter - ni - ty".............   E - ter - ni-

E - ter - ni - ty

ty,   E - ter - ni - ty,   Where we may spend   e - ter - ni - ty.
ty,   E - ter - ni - ty,   A mes-sage from   e - ter - ni - ty.
ty,   E - ter - ni - ty,   And sing thro' all   e - ter - ni - ty.
ty,   E - ter - ni - ty,   And dwell in blest   e - ter - ni - ty.

No. 51. Truth Triumphant.

Grace Reed Oliver.

1. My soul has seen a vis - ion of the conquest of the world, When
2. No more shall strife and ha - tred bring dis - hon - or to our God, For
3. The des - ert place shall blos-som, and the wil-der-ness re-joice; The

Sa - tan and His forc - es from their bat-tle-ments are hurled, And o'er the
righteousness, whose work is peace, shall spread her wings a-broad; And they who
lame shall leap, the blind shall see, the dumb lift up their voice; The floods shall

land the Bi - ble, like a sig - nal flag unfurled, Speaks loy - al-ty to Christ.
win the con-quest are the bear - ers of the word, In loy - al-ty to Christ.
clap their hands, the earth shall make a joy-ful noise, In loy - al-ty to Christ.

CHORUS.

We shall see the truth so glorious Over all the earth vic-to - ri - ous,

For the standard lift - ed o - ver us Is loy - al - ty to Christ.

No. 52. O Love Divine.

Maud Frazer.   **Chas. H. Gabriel.**

1. Dear Lord, my heart has heard Thy call! Be-fore Thy cross I prostrate fall
2. Thy plead-ing eyes have look'd on me, Thy sweet voice said, "I died for thee;"
3. I spurned Thy grace and far did stray, Yet "child, come home," I heard Thee say;
4. O Love, my star in sor-row's night, When foes as-sail, my sword of might;

And un - to Thee sur-ren-der all, O Love di - vine, O Love di - vine!
No more a reb - el can I be, O Love di - vine, O Love di - vine!
Love came to meet me on the way, O Love di - vine, O Love di - vine!
O Love, my joy, my life, my light, O Love di - vine, O Love di - vine!

CHORUS.

O Love di - vine, so full, so free, Thy wondrous pow'r has conquered me!

For ev - er - more my heart is Thine, O Love di - vine, O Love di - vine!

No. 53.

"Whosoever Will."

P. P. B.   P. P. Bliss.

1. "Who-so-ev - er heareth," shout, shout the sound! Spread the bless-ed ti - dings
2. Who-so-ev - er com - eth need not de - lay, Now the door is o - pen,
3. "Who-so-ev - er will," the prom - ise se - cure, "Who - so - ev - er will," for

all the world a - round; Spread the joy - ful news wher - ev - er man is found:
en - ter while you may; Je - sus is the true, the on - ly Liv - ing Way:
ev - er must en-dure; "Who - so-ev - er will," 'tis life for - ev - er-more:

Chorus.

"Who - so - ev - er will may come." "Who-so-ev - er will, who - so-ev-er will,"

Send the proc-la - ma - tion o - ver vale and hill; 'Tis a lov - ing Fa - ther

calls the wan - d'rer home: "Who - so - ev - er will, may come."

No. 54. My Rest.

Fanny J. Crosby.   Jno. R. Sweney.

1. Deep and deep-er fell the shad-ows, Near-er seem'd the gold-en strand,
2. Near-er seem'd the shin-ing por-tals, But the Mas-ter said to me,
3. In the si-lent hours of mid-night, When my waking tho'ts take wings,

And 'my trust-ing heart was wait-ing, Pass-ive in my Savior's hands;
"There are sheaves that must be garner'd Ere the reap-ing dawns for thee;
O the tran-quil peace He gives me, And the hallow'd songs He brings!

O how bright-ly o'er my spir-it Came a radiance from a-far,
Yet I knew that thou wert wea-ry, And I bade thy heart re-pose
He has crown'd me with His bless-ing, And I now by faith can say,

Like the blush of ear-ly morn-ing, Like the ris-ing of a star.
By a healing stream that mur-murs Where the Rose of Shar-on grows."
I am go-ing forth with vig-or, Still re-joic-ing on my way.

CHORUS.

I was waiting,..... calm-ly waiting,... Not a fear was in my breast;

I was waiting,   calmly waiting.

My Rest.

I had trusted ...... my Redeemer, ... And in Him was now my rest.
I had trusted   my Redeemer,

No, Not One.

No. 55.

Johnson Oatman, Jr.

USED BY PERMISSION OF GEO. C. HUGG,
OWNER OF COPYRIGHT.

Geo. C. Hugg.

Slow, and with feeling.

1. There's not a friend like the low-ly Je-sus,   No, not one! no, not one!
2. No friend like Him is so high and ho-ly,   No, not one! no, not one!
3. There's not an hour that He is not near us,   No, not one! no, not one!
4. Did ev-er saint find this Friend for-sake him?   No, not one! no, not one!

Fine.

None else could heal all our souls' dis-eas-es,   No, not one! no, not one!
And yet no friend is so meek and low-ly,   No, not one! no, not one!
No night so dark but His love can cheer us,   No, not one! no, not one!
Or sin-ner find that He would not take him?   No, not one! no, not one!

D. S.—There's not a friend like the low-ly Je-sus,   No, not one! no, not one!

CHORUS.

D. S.

Je-sus knows all a-bout our struggles,   He will guide till the day is done;

No. 56. Count It All Joy.

W. E. M.

Wm. Edie Marks.

1. Count it all joy to bear the cross of Je - sus! Just a lit - tle bur-den
2. Count it all joy when sore-ly tried and tempted! He has promised grace to
3. Count it all joy when walking thro' the val - ley! E - ven in the night the

for the Mas-ter's sake; Soon there will be ex - ceed-ing weight of glo - ry
help in time of need; Trust - ing in God, press ev - er on to con-quer,
Lord will give a song; Je - sus can turn thy sor - row in - to glad-ness;

CHORUS.

For His tried and faith-ful serv-ants to par-take.
He will al-ways prove to be a friend in - deed. Count it all joy, count it
Praise and hon-or un - to Him for aye be - long.

all joy, Count it joy to serve the Lord from day to day; Count it all joy

to bear the cross of Je-sus, All things work for good to those who love the Lord.

No. 57. There is Joy.

BY PER. OF SILVER BURDETTE & CO.
OWNERS OF COPYRIGHT.

Margaret Moody.   W. A. Ogden.

1. When a sin-ner comes, as a sin-ner may, There is joy, ...
2. When a soul is born in the king-dom bright, There is joy, ...
3. When a pil-grim comes to the riv-er wide, There is joy, ...

There is joy,

there is joy; .... When he turns to God in the gos-pel way,
there is joy; .... When it walks by faith in the gos-pel light,
there is joy; .... When he dwells se-cure on the oth-er side,

there is joy;

CHORUS.

There is joy, ... there is joy. There is joy a-mong the

There is joy,

an-gels, And their hearts with mu-sic ring, ... When a

mu-sic ring,

sin-ner comes re-pent-ing, Bend-ing low be-fore the King.

No. 58. For a Smile.

James Rowe.

Wm. Edie Marks.

1. In this world of sin and strife, In this cold and storm-y life, Where we
2. Friends to help them they have had, Whose sweet voices made them glad, As their
3. Heav-y burdens press them down, Stormy skies a-bove them frown, And the

see so much of troub-le all the while; There are those who, day by day,
mu - sic would the wear-y hours be - guile; One by one they all have gone,
path seems growing dark-er ev -'ry mile; No one points them to the throne,

Tread a lone-ly, friendless way, Vainly waiting, vain-ly watching for a smile.
Left a - lone to wan-der on, Vainly waiting, vain-ly watching for a smile.
So they wan-der all a-lone, Vainly waiting, vain-ly watching for a smile.

CHORUS.

For a smile, for a smile, They are waiting, they are watching for a smile;
For a smile, for a smile. for a smile;

For a smile, for a smile, They are waiting, they are watching for a smile.
For a smile, for a smile,

No. 59. There's a Great Day Coming.

USED BY PER W. L. THOMPSON & CO. EAST LIVERPOOL, O., AND CHICAGO.

W L. T.   Will L. Thompson

1. There's a great day com-ing, A great day com-ing, There's a great day com-ing by and by; When the saints and the sin - ners shall be part - ed right and left, Are you read - y for that day to come?

2. There's a bright day com-ing, A bright day com-ing, There's a bright day com-ing by and by; But its bright-ness shall on - ly come to them that love the Lord, Are you read - y for that day to come?

3. There's a sad day com-ing, A sad day com-ing, There's a sad day com-ing by and by; When the sin - ner shall hear his doom, "de- part, I know ye not," Are you read - y for that day to come?

CHORUS.

Are you read - y? Are you read - y? Are you read - y for the judg-ment day? Are you ready? Are you read - y for the judgment day?

No. 60. A Sinner Made Whole.

W. M. Lighthall.

Chas. H. Gabriel.

1. There's a song in my heart that my lips can-not sing, 'Tis praise in the
2. I shall stand one day faultless and pure by His throne, Transformed from my
3. All the mu - sic of heav-en, so per-fect and sweet, Will blend with my

high - est to Je-sus, my King; Its mu-sic each moment is thrilling my soul,
im - age conformed to His own; Then I shall find words for the song of my soul,
song and will make it complete; Thro' a - ges un-end-ing the ech-oes will roll,

CHORUS.

For I was a sin-ner, but Christ made me whole, A sin-ner made whole! a

Rit.

sinner made whole! The Savior hath bought me and ransomed my soul! My heart it is

Rit.

singing, the anthem is ringing, For I was a sinner, but Christ made me whole.

No. 61. There Shall Be Showers of Blessing.

El Nathan.

James McGranahan.

1. "There shall be show-ers of bless-ing"—This is the prom-ise of love;
2. "There shall be show-ers of bless-ing"— Pre-cious re-viv-ing a - gain,
3. "There shall be show-ers of bless-ing"—Send them up - on us, O Lord!
4. "There shall be show-ers of bless-ing"— O that to - day they might fall,

There shall be sea-sons re - fresh - ing, Sent from the Sav - ior a - bove.
O - ver the hills and the val - leys Sound of a - bun-dance of rain.
Grant to us now a re - fresh - ing, Come, and now hon - or Thy Word!
Now as to God we're con-fess - ing, Now as on Je - sus we call!

CHORUS.

Show - ers of bless - ing, Show-ers of bless-ing we need;

Show - ers, show - ers

Mer - cy-drops round us are fall - ing, But for the show-ers we plead.

No. 62. I Want to Go There.

Rev. D. S. Rev. D. Sullins.

1. They tell of a cit-y far up in the sky, I want to go
2. Its gates are all pearl, its streets are all gold, I want to go
3. When the old ship of Zi-on shall make her last trip, I want to be
4. When Je-sus is crowned the King of all kings, I want to be

there, I do; 'Tis built in the land of "the sweet by and by," I
there, I do; The Lamb is the light of that cit-y we're told, I
there, I do; With heads all un-cov-ered to greet the old ship, I
there, I do; With shout-ing and clap-ping till all heav-en rings, I

want to go there, don't you? There Je-sus has gone to pre-pare us a
want to go there, don't you? Death robs us all here, there none ev-er
want to be there, don't you? When all the ship's company meet on the
want to be there, don't you? Hal-le-lu-jah! we'll shout a - gain and a-

home, I want to go there, I do; Where sick-ness nor sor-row nor
die, I want to go there, I do; Where loved ones will nev-er a-
strand, I want to be there, I do; "With songs on our lips and with
gain, I want to be there, I do; And close with the cho-rus, A-

I Want to Go There.

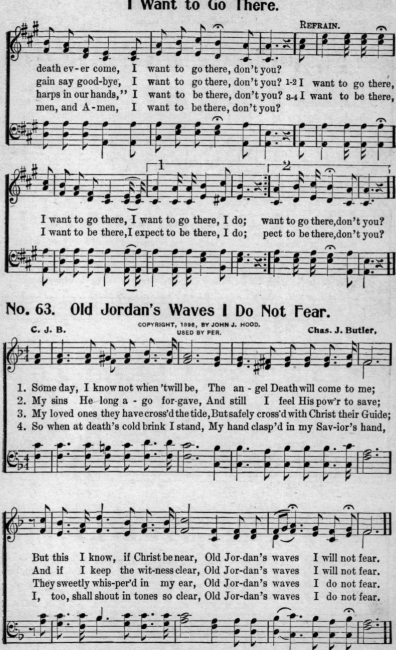

death ev - er come, I want to go there, don't you?
gain say good-bye, I want to go there, don't you? 1-2 I want to go there,
harps in our hands," I want to be there, don't you? 3-4 I want to be there,
men, and A - men, I want to be there, don't you?

I want to go there, I want to go there, I do; want to go there, don't you?
I want to be there, I expect to be there, I do; pect to be there, don't you?

No. 63. Old Jordan's Waves I Do Not Fear.

C. J. B.

COPYRIGHT, 1896, BY JOHN J. HOOD.
USED BY PER.

Chas. J. Butler,

1. Some day, I know not when 'twill be, The an - gel Death will come to me;
2. My sins He long a - go for-gave, And still I feel His pow'r to save;
3. My loved ones they have cross'd the tide, But safely cross'd with Christ their Guide;
4. So when at death's cold brink I stand, My hand clasp'd in my Sav-ior's hand,

But this I know, if Christ be near, Old Jor-dan's waves I will not fear.
And if I keep the wit-ness clear, Old Jor-dan's waves I will not fear.
They sweetly whis-per'd in my ear, Old Jor-dan's waves I do not fear.
I, too, shall shout in tones so clear, Old Jor-dan's waves I do not fear.

Ashamed of Jesus.

Joseph Griggs.

E. O. Excell.

1. Je - sus, and shall it ev - er be A mor - tal
2. A - shamed of Je - sus! soon - er far Let ev - 'ning
3. A - shamed of Je - sus! that dear Friend, On whom my
4. A - shamed of Je - sus! yes, I may, When I've no

man a - shamed of Thee? A - shamed of Thee, whom
blush to own a star; He sheds the beams of
hopes of heav'n de - pend? No! when I blush be
guilt to wash a - way, No tear to wipe, no

an - gels praise, Whose glo - ries shine thro' end - less days?
light di - vine O'er this be - night - ed soul of mine.
this my shame, That I no more re - vere His name.
good to crave, No fears to quell, no soul to save.

CHORUS.

A-shamed .... of Je - sus, I nev-er, I nev-er will be;

A-shamed of Je-sus, a-shamed of Je-sus, I nev-er, I nev-er, I nev-er will be;

*Tenor and Bass sing the upper *large* notes; the Sop. and Alto the lower. Small notes with the large ones for organist.

Ashamed of Jesus.

For Je - - sus, my Sav - - ior, is not ashamed of me.
For Je - sus, my Sav-ior, for Je - sus, my Sav-ior.

No. 65. He Leadeth Me.

J. H. Gilmore.   Wm. B. Bradbury.

1. He lead-eth me: O bless-ed tho't! O words with heav'nly com-fort fraught!
2. Sometimes 'mid scenes of deepest gloom, Sometimes where Eden's bowers bloom,
3. Lord, I would clasp Thy hand in mine, Nor ev - er mur-mur or re - pine;
4. And when my task on earth is done, When by Thy grace the vict'ry's won,

What-e'er I do, wher-e'er I be, Still 'tis God's hand that lead-eth me.
By wa - ters still, o'er troub-led sea—Still 'tis God's hand that lead-eth me.
Con-tent, what-ev - er lot I see, Since 'tis my God that lead-eth me.
E'en death's cold wave I will not flee, Since God thro' Jor - dan lead-eth me.

CHORUS.

He leadeth me, He lead-eth me, By His own hand He leadeth me;
His faithful follow'r I would be, For by His hand He   leadeth me.

Why Not To-day?

J. E. Rankin, D. D.   E. O. Excell.

1. You think the house of prayer so sweet, (the prayer so sweet,) So sweet the voice of sa - cred song; (so sweet the song;) You turn a - way re - luct - ant feet, (re - luct - ant feet,) As tho' the hour you would prolong; [the hour prolong:] And yet your soul is un - for - giv'n, No ti - tle yet have you for heav'n; You

2. You think you love God's people now, (you love them now,) You love their com-pa - ny to share; (you love to share;) You love be - fore His throne to bow, [you love to bow.] And list - en to their humble pray'r; [their humble pray'r;] Why should you pause and hes - i - tate, Un - til per-haps it be too late? You

3. There is no work be - yond the grave, (be - yond the grave,) There is no la - bor or de - vice, (there's no de - vice,) There is no pow'r can reach to save, [no pow'r to save,] There is no ran-som there or price; [there is no price;] No gos - pel word or gospel song, No house of God where Christians throng; You

Why Not To-day?

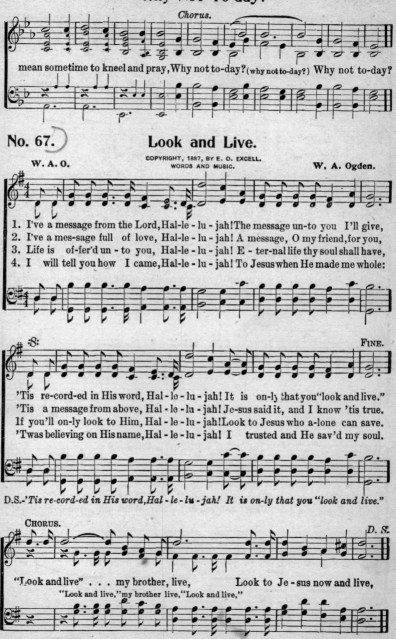

Chorus.

mean sometime to kneel and pray, Why not to-day? (why not to-day?) Why not to-day?

No. 67. Look and Live.

W. A. O.

COPYRIGHT, 1887, BY E. O. EXCELL.
WORDS AND MUSIC.

W. A. Ogden.

1. I've a message from the Lord, Hal-le-lu-jah! The message un-to you I'll give,
2. I've a mes-sage full of love, Hal-le-lu-jah! A message, O my friend, for you,
3. Life is of-fer'd un-to you, Hal-le-lu-jah! E-ter-nal life thy soul shall have,
4. I will tell you how I came, Hal-le-lu-jah! To Jesus when He made me whole:

FINE.

'Tis re-cord-ed in His word, Hal-le-lu-jah! It is on-ly that you "look and live."
'Tis a message from above, Hal-le-lu-jah! Je-sus said it, and I know 'tis true.
If you'll on-ly look to Him, Hal-le-lu-jah! Look to Jesus who a-lone can save.
'Twas believing on His name, Hal-le-lu-jah! I trusted and He sav'd my soul.

D.S.—'Tis re-cord-ed in His word, Hal-le-lu-jah! It is on-ly that you "look and live."

CHORUS.

D. S.

"Look and live" . . . my brother, live, Look to Je-sus now and live,
"Look and live," my brother live, "Look and live,"

What Will You Do?

E. O. E.

E. O. Excell.

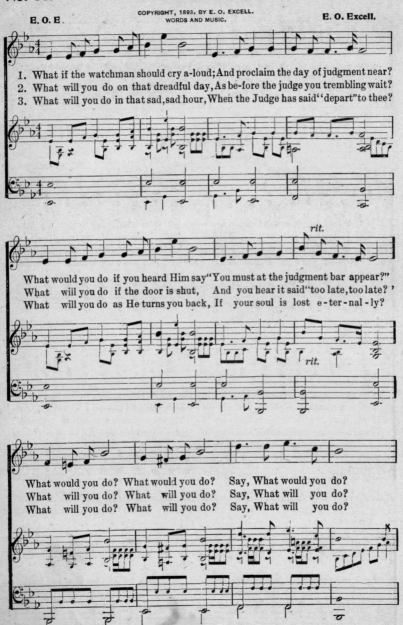

1. What if the watchman should cry a-loud; And proclaim the day of judgment near?
2. What will you do on that dreadful day, As be-fore the judge you trembling wait?
3. What will you do in that sad, sad hour, When the Judge has said "depart" to thee?

What would you do if you heard Him say "You must at the judgment bar appear?"
What will you do if the door is shut, And you hear it said "too late, too late?"
What will you do as He turns you back, If your soul is lost e-ter-nal-ly?

What would you do? What would you do? Say, What would you do?
What will you do? What will you do? Say, What will you do?
What will you do? What will you do? Say, What will you do?

What Will You Do?

mf   *rit.*

What would you do if you heard Him say, "You must at the judgment bar appear?"
What will you do if the door is shut, And you hear it said "too late, too late?"
What will you do as He turns you back, If your soul is lost e-ter-nal-ly?

mf   *rit.*

No. 69. Anywhere With Jesus.

John R. Clements.   E. O Excell.

1. I'll go an-y-where, my Sav-ior, If Thou wilt make it clear; I will
2. I'll do an-y-thing, my Sav-ior, That hon-or brings to Thee; I will
3. I'll be an-y-thing, my Sav-ior, In sta-tion high or low; I will
4. I'll hold ev-'ry-thing, my Sav-ior, A sa-cred trust of Thine; And the

CHORUS.

tell sal-va-tion's sto-ry To lost ones far and near.
fol-low close Thy lead-ing Wher-e'er it tak-eth me. An-y-where, my
toil, or wait, or suf-fer, If Thou dost will it so.
tal-ents to me giv-en, I'll count them not as mine.

Sav-ior, Anywhere for Thee, Anywhere and ev'rywhere, As Thou leadest me.

No. 70. Lead Me Gently Home, Father.

W. L. T.

W. L. Thompson.

SOLO OR DUET. *ad lib.*

1. Lead me gen-tly home, Father, Lead me gen-tly home, When life's toils are end-ed, And parting days have come, Sin no more shall tempt me, Ne'er from Thee I'll roam, If Thou'lt on-ly lead me, Father, Lead me gen-tly home.

2. Lead me gen-tly home, Father, Lead me gen-tly home, In life's dark-est hours, Father, When life's troubles come, Keep my feet from wand'ring, Lest from Thee I roam, Lest I fall up-on the wayside, Lead me gen-tly home.

rit. *p*

REFRAIN.

Lead me gen-tly home, Fa-ther Lead me gen-tly,
Lead me gen-tly home, Fa-ther, Lead me gen-tly home, Fa-ther,

Lest I fall up-on the way-side, Lead me gen-tly home.
gen-tly home.

The Cross is Not Greater.

B. B. COPYRIGHT PROPERTY OF BALLINGTON BOOTH. Ballington Booth.

1. The cross that He gave may be heav-y, But it ne'er outweighs His grace;
2. The thorns in my path are not sharper Than composed His crown for me;
3. The light of His love shineth bright-er, As it falls on paths of woe,
4. His will I have joy in ful-fill-ing, As I'm walk-ing in His sight,

The storm that I fear'd may surround me, But it ne'er ex-cludes His face.
The cup that I drink not more bit-ter Than He drank in Geth-sem-a-ne.
The toil of my work groweth light-er, As I stoop to raise the low.
My all to the blood I am bring-ing, It a-lone can keep me right.

CHORUS.

The cross is not great-er than His grace, The storm can-not

hide His bless-ed face; I am sat-is-fied to know That with

Je-sus here be-low, I can con-quer ev-'ry foe.

No. 72. My Savior First of All.

Fanny J. Crosby.

Jno. R. Sweney.

1. When my life work is end - ed, and I cross the swell-ing tide, When the
2. Oh, the soul-thrill-ing rapt-ure when I view His bless - ed face, And the
3. Oh, the dear ones in glo - ry, how they beck-on me to come, And our
4. Thro' the gates to the cit - y, in a robe of spot - less white He will

bright and glorious morning I shall see, I shall know my Re-deemer when I
lus - ter of His kind - ly beaming eye; How my full heart will praise Him for the
part - ing at the riv - er I re - call; To the sweet vales of E-den they will
lead me where no tears will ev - er fall; In the glad song of a - ges I shall

reach the oth - er side, And His smile will be the first to wel - come me.
mer - cy, love and grace, That pre-pare for me a man-sion in the sky.
sing my wel-come home; But I long to meet my Sav-ior first of all.
min - gle with de - light; But I long to meet my Sav-ior first of all.

CHORUS.

I shall know Him, I shall know Him, And redeem'd by His side I shall stand,

I shall know Him

My Savior First of All.

I shall know   Him, I shall know Him By the print of the nails in His hand.

I shall know Him,

No. 73.

Beautiful Isle.

Jessie B. Pounds.

J. S. Fearis.

1. Some-where the sun   is   shin - ing, Some-where the song - birds dwell;
2. Some-where the day   is   lon - ger, Some-where the task   is   done;
3. Some-where the load   is   lift - ed, Close by an   o - pen gate;

Hush, then, thy sad   re - pin - ing, God lives, and all . is   well.
Some-where the heart is stron - ger, Some-where the guer - don won.
Some-where the clouds are rift - ed, Some-where the an - gels wait.

CHORUS.

Some - where,   Some - where, Beau-ti - ful Isle   of Some-where!

Some-where, beau-ti - ful, beau - ti - ful Isle,

Land of the true, where we live a - new,—Beau-ti-ful Isle   of Some-where!

Standing On the Promises.

R. K. C. COPYRIGHT, 1886, BY JOHN J. HOOD. USED BY PER. R Kelso Carter.

1. Standing on the prom-is-es of Christ my King, Thro' e-ter-nal
2. Standing on the prom-is-es that can not fail, When the howl-ing
3. Standing on the prom-is-es of Christ the Lord, Bound to Him e-
4. Standing on the prom-is-es I can not fall, List-'ning ev-'ry

a-ges let His praises ring; Glo-ry in the high-est, I will shout and sing,
storms of doubt and fear as-sail, By the liv-ing word of God I shall prevail,
ter-nal-ly by love's strong cord, O-ver-com-ing dai-ly with the Spirit's sword,
mo-ment to the Spirit's call, Rest-ing in my Sav-ior, as my all in all,

CHORUS.

Standing on the prom-is-es of God. Stand - ing, stand -
Standing on the prom-is-es, standing on the

ing, Standing on the prom-is-es of God my Sav-ior; Stand -
prom-is-es, Stand-ing on the

ing, stand - ing, I'm standing on the prom-is-es of God.
prom-is-es, stand-ing on the prom-is-es

No. 75.

No Room in the Inn.

A. L. Skilton.

E. Grace Updegraff.

1. No beau-ti-ful cham-ber, No soft cra-dle bed, No place but a
2. No sweet con-se-cra-tion, No seek-ing His part, No hu-mil-i-
3. No one to re-ceive Him, No welcome while here, No balm to re-

man-ger, No where for His Head; No prais-es, of glad-ness,
a-tion, No place in the heart; No tho't of the Sav-ior,
lieve Him, No staff but a spear; No seek-ing His treas-ure,

No tho't of their sin, No glo-ry, but sad-ness, No room in the inn.
No sor-row for sin, No pray'r for His fa-vor, No room in the inn.
No weeping for sin, No do-ing His pleas-ure, No room in the inn.

rit.

CHORUS.

No room, no room for Je-sus, Oh, give Him wel-come free,

rit.

Lest you should hear at Heav-en's gate, "There is no room for Thee."

That Sweet Story.

WORDS AND MUSIC COPYRIGHT, 1905, BY E. O. EXCELL.
INTERNATIONAL COPYRIGHT SECURED.

James Rowe.

E. O. Excell.

1. I once heard a sweet sto-ry of won-der-ful love, And it lift-ed the
2. Tho' a-far I had wander'd in darkness and sin, And tho' helpless, and
3. That sweet sto-ry of Je-sus Who died on the tree Will be told on e-

cross that I bore, Made me think of the home and the dear ones a-bove;
wea-ry, and poor, This sweet sto-ry left light, hope and gladness with-in;
ter-ni-ty's shore; How He came as a ran-som for you and for me;

CHORUS.

I am long-ing to hear it once more. I am long-ing to hear it once

more; The sto-ry re-peat o'er and o'er;...... It is rapt-ure di-
once more; o'er and o'er;

vine, to know He is mine; I am longing to hear it once more.

No. 77. Shout the Tidings.

Arr. by J. P. Powell.

1. Shout the ti-dings of sal-va-tion, To the a-ged and the young;
2. Shout the ti-dings of sal-va-tion, O'er the prairies of the West;
3. Shout the ti-dings of sal-va-tion, Min-gling with the o cean's roar;
4. Shout the ti-dings of sal-va-tion, O'er the is lands of the sea;

Till the pre-cious in - vi - ta - tion, Wak-ens ev-'ry heart and tongue.
Till each gath'ring con-gre - ga - tion, With the gos-pel sound is blest.
Till the ships or ev-'ry na - tion Bear the news from shore to shore.
Till in hum-ble ad - o - ra - tion, All to Christ shall bow the knee.

Chorus.

Send the sound The earth a-round From the ris-ing to the set-ting of the sun,

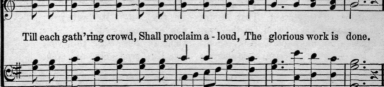

Till each gath'ring crowd, Shall proclaim a - loud, The glorious work is done.

No. 78. That Old, Old, Story is True.

D. B. Watkins.   E. O. Excell.

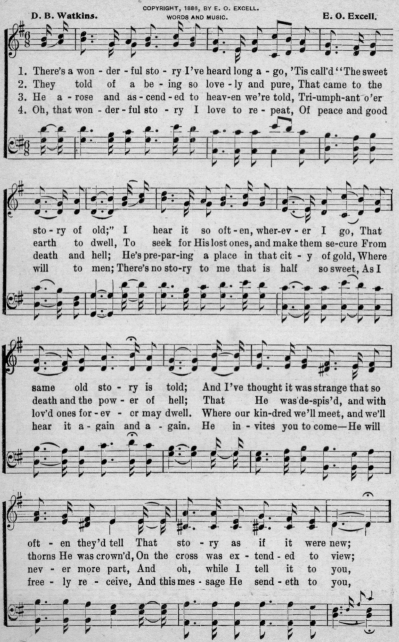

1. There's a won - der - ful sto - ry I've heard long a - go, 'Tis call'd "The sweet
2. They told of a be - ing so love - ly and pure, That came to the
3. He a - rose and as - cend - ed to heav-en we're told, Tri - umph-ant o'er
4. Oh, that won - der - ful sto - ry I love to re - peat, Of peace and good

sto - ry of old;" I hear it so oft-en, wher-ev-er I go, That
earth to dwell, To seek for His lost ones, and make them se-cure From
death and hell; He's pre-par-ing a place in that cit - y of gold, Where
will to men; There's no sto-ry to me that is half so sweet, As I

same old sto - ry is told; And I've thought it was strange that so
death and the pow - er of hell; That He was de-spis'd, and with
lov'd ones for - ev - er may dwell. Where our kin-dred we'll meet, and we'll
hear it a - gain and a - gain. He in - vites you to come—He will

oft - en they'd tell That sto - ry as if it were new;
thorns He was crown'd, On the cross was ex - tend - ed to view;
nev - er more part, And oh, while I tell it to you,
free - ly re - ceive, And this mes - sage He send - eth to you,

That Old, Old Story is True.

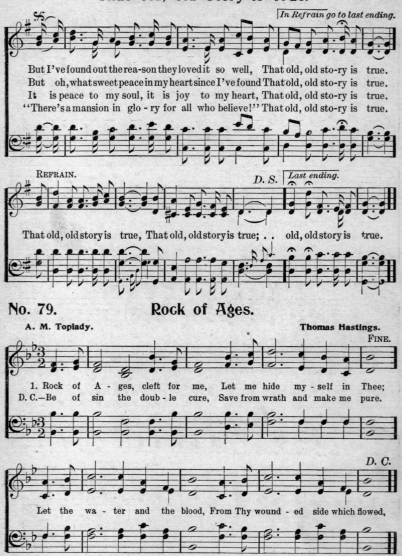

In Refrain go to last ending.

But I've found out the reason they loved it so well, That old, old sto-ry is true.
But oh, what sweet peace in my heart since I've found That old, old sto-ry is true.
It is peace to my soul, it is joy to my heart, That old, old sto-ry is true.
"There's a mansion in glo-ry for all who believe!" That old, old sto-ry is true.

REFRAIN.

D. S. | *Last ending.*

That old, old story is true, That old, old story is true; .. old, old story is true.

No. 79. Rock of Ages.

A. M. Toplady.

Thomas Hastings.

FINE.

1. Rock of A - ges, cleft for me, Let me hide my - self in Thee;
D. C.—Be of sin the doub - le cure, Save from wrath and make me pure.

D. C.

Let the wa - ter and the blood, From Thy wound - ed side which flowed,

2 Could my tears forever flow,
Could my zeal no languor know,
These for sin could not atone,
Thou must save, and Thou alone:
In my hand no price I bring,
Simply to Thy cross I cling.

3 While I draw this fleeting breath,
When my eyes shall close in death,
When I rise to worlds unknown,
And behold Thee on Thy throne,
Rock of Ages, cleft for me,
Let me hide myself in Thee.

No. 80. Will There be any Stars?

E. E. Hewitt.　　　　　　　　　　　　Jno. R. Sweney.

1. I am think-ing to-day of that beau-ti - ful land I shall reach when the
2. In the strength of the Lord let me la - bor and pray, Let me watch as a
3. Oh, what joy it will be when His face I be-hold, Liv-ing gems at His

sun go - eth down; When thro' won-der-ful grace by my Sav-ior I stand,
win - ner of souls; That bright stars may be mine in the glo - ri - ous day,
feet to lay down; It would sweeten my bliss in the cit - y of gold,

CHORUS.

Will there be an - y stars in my crown?
When His praise like the sea-bil-low rolls. Will there be an - y stars, an - y
Should there be an - y stars in my crown.

stars in my crown When at ev-'ning the sun go-eth down? . . . . . . When I
go-eth down?

wake with the blest In the mansions of rest, Will there be an-y stars in my crown?
an-y stars in my crown?

No. 81. Since I Have Been Redeemed.

WORDS AND MUSIC.

E. O. E.   E. O. Excell.

1. I have a song I love to sing, Since I have been re-deem'd,
2. I have a Christ that sat-is-fies, Since I have been re-deem'd,
3. I have a Wit-ness bright and clear, Since I have been re-deem'd,
4. I have a home pre-pared for me, Since I have been re-deem'd,

Of my Re-deem-er, Sav-ior, King, Since I have been re-deem'd.
To do His will my high-est prize, Since I have been re-deem'd.
Dis-pell-ing ev-'ry doubt and fear, Since I have been re-deem'd.
Where I shall dwell e-ter-nal-ly, Since I have been re-deem'd.

CHORUS.

Since I .... have been re-deem'd, Since I have been redeem'd,
Since I have been re-deem'd, since I have been re-deem'd,

I will glo-ry in His name, Since I .... have been re-
Since, I have been re-deem'd, Since

deem'd, I will glo-ry in my Sav-ior's name.
I have been re-deem'd,

No. 82. Precious Promise.

Nathaniel Niles.

P. P. Bliss.

1. Pre - cious prom-ise God hath giv - en To the wea - ry pass - er - by,
2. When temp-ta - tions al - most win thee, And thy trust - ed watch-ers fly,
3. When thy se - cret hope have per-ished In the grave of years gone by,
4. When the shades of life are fall - ing, And the hour has come to die,

On the way from earth to heav - en, "I will guide thee with mine eye."
Let this prom - ise ring with - in thee, "I will guide thee with mine eye."
Let this prom - ise still be cher-ished, "I will guide thee with mine eye."
Hear the trust - y Pi - lot call - ing, "I will guide thee with mine eye."

CHORUS.

I will guide thee, I will guide thee, I will guide thee with mine eye;

On the road from earth to heav - en, I will guide thee with mine eye.

No. 83. Where Are You Going?

OWNED BY CHAS. REIGN SCOVILLE.
COPYRIGHT, 1906, BY SCOVILLE & SMITH.

F. H. C.

Flora Hamilton Cassel.

1. Where are you go-ing, my broth-er, Wan-der-ing day by day?
2. Ea-sy and smooth is the down grade, Steep is the up-ward way,
3. Nar-row and straight is the right way, That leads to the land of bliss,

Swift-ly your foot-steps are pass-ing on O-ver the downward way.
Broad is the road which will lead to death, Broth-er, no more de-lay.
Glo-ry and beau-ty and bright-ness, Far bet-ter home than this!

Oh, turn from your path to-day, Broth-er, no long-er stray. The
Tho' hidden, there's dan-ger near, List to the warn-ing clear. There's
Then fly from the wrath to come, Haste to the heav'n-ly home; Thy

CHO.—*Turn from your path to-day, Broth-er, no long-er stray. The*

road will be bright, If you turn to the right, Oh, broth-er, no long-er
hor-ror and fright With the darkness of night, Oh, broth-er, the mes-sage
Sav-ior a-waits At the pearl-y gates, Oh, broth-er, no long-er

road will be bright, If you turn to the right, Oh, broth-er, no long-er

Chorus D. S.

FINE.

stray. Go-ing, go-ing, O-ver the downward way, Oh,
hear. Go-ing, go-ing, O-ver the downward way, Oh,
roam. Go-ing, go-ing, O-ver the downward way, Oh,

stray.

No. 84.   Jesus Will do the Same for You.

J. T. Latta.

Ira B. Wilson.

1. When the bless-ed Sav - ior Saw me far a - stray, Ten - der - ly He
2. When the bless-ed Sav - ior Found me in de - spair, O-ver-whelm'd with
3. When the bless-ed Sav - ior Took a - way my sin, With His blood He

sought me, Call - ing night and day; On the wings of mer - cy,
tri - als, And with woe and care; Then He gave me cour - age,
washed me, Made me pure with - in; By His Ho - ly Spir - it

S.   FINE.

To my res - cue flew, And to - day He's will-ing to do the same for you.
Did my strength re - new, And to - day He's will-ing to do the same for you.
Cleans'd me thro'and thro', And to - day He's will-ing to do the same for you.

D.S.—*No one else could do, And to - day He's will-ing to do the same for you.*

CHORUS.

Je - sus Christ my Sav - ior will do the same for you, Je - sus Christ my

D. S.

Sav - ior will do the same for you; He has done for me what

All for Jesus.

Rev. J. B. Atchinson.

E. O. Excell.

1. All, yes, all I give to Je - sus, It be - longs to Him;
2. All, yes, all I give to Je - sus, It be - longs to Him;
3. All, yes, all I give to Je - sus, It be - longs to Him;
4. All, yes, all I give to Je - sus, It be - longs to Him;

All my heart I give to Je - sus It be - longs to Him;
All my voice I give to Je - sus It be - longs to Him;
All my love I give to Je - sus It be - longs to Him;
All my life I give to Je - sus It be - longs to Him;

Ev - er - more to be His dwell - ing, Ev - er - more His prais - es swell - ing,
Plead - ing for the young and hoar - y, Tell - ing of His pow'r and glo - ry,
Lov - ing Him for love un - ceas - ing, For His mer - cy e'er in - creas - ing,
Hour by hour I'll live for Je - sus, Day by day I'll work for Je - sus,

Ev - er - more His good - ness tell - ing, It be - longs to Him.
Sing - ing o'er and o'er the sto - ry, It be - longs to Him.
For His watch - care nev - er ceas - ing, It be - longs to Him.
Ev - er - more I'll hon - or Je - sus, It be - longs to Him.

No. 86. What Have I Done for Jesus?

Arranged by
Grace Medbury and George Ogden.

COPYRIGHT, 1909, BY CHAS. REIGN SCOVILLE.

Words and music by
Frederick Howard.

1. Have I spok-en words of love, Or sel - fish have I gone? Have I made some
2. Have I held the Sav-ior's face Enshrin'd with-in my heart? Have I lived for
3. Traveler worn with wea-ry feet, Be - hold the Master's face; Sin-sick soul, all

blackness white, Or sung a cheer-ful song? Have I bro't a smile of hope, Or
gain of gold, My life ab-sorbed in mart? Have I vis - it-ed the sick, Their
tem - pest-torn, Re - pose in His em-brace; Wea-ry ones, heart-aching ones, Be-

wiped sad tears a - way? Have I done a sin - gle thing In Jesus' name to-day?
fev - er to al - lay? Have I done a sin - gle thing In Jesus' name to-day?
hold, His is the way, Let me lead you to the Christ In Jesus' name to-day.

Chorus.

Fa - ther, in pen - i-tence plead-ing, For-give-ness I ask not in vain;
3rd Fa - ther, thy name I have spo-ken, I've walk'd close beside thee all day,

To mor-row, if spared thro' Thy mer-cy, I'll serve Thee a-gain and a - gain.
I've clung to the hem of Thy gar-ment, In fear lest I lose my way.

What Have I Done for Jesus?

I'll lift up the bruis-ed and fall-en, I'll lead the blind to the light;
I've told oth-ers that sweet old sto-ry From heav'n they've seen Thy light;—

For to-day I've done nothing for Je-sus—Hold me close in Your arms to-night.
To - day I've done something for Je-sus, Let me rest in His arms to - night.

No. 87. Everything for Jesus.

Flora E. Breck.

Carl Fischer.

1. Ev-'ry-thing for Je - sus! Un - to Him I give All I have and hope for;
2. Ev-'ry-thing for Je - sus! I will con - se-crate Life, and love, and serv-ice,
3. Ev-'ry-thing for Je - sus! Ev - 'ry-thing I know, On my lov - ing Sav - ior

CHORUS.

'Tis for Him I live.
Ere it be too late.   Ev-'ry-thing for Je - sus, All to Christ my King!
Glad - ly I be - stow.

To Him who gave so much for me, I will give Him ev - 'ry - thing.

Harvest Song!

WORDS AND MUSIC COPYRIGHT, 1907, BY CHAS. H. GABRIEL.
E. O. EXCELL, OWNER.

C. H. G.

Chas. H. Gabriel.

1. Look, the har-vest field is teem-ing With the rich and ripened grain;
2. In the mar-kets and the by-ways, Whil-ing pre-cious hours a-way,
3. Hear ye not the faith-ful sing-ing Of the la-bor and the yield?

Wide it spreads be-fore us, Bright the sky is o'er us; In the
Ma-ny stand com-plain-ing, I-dle still re-main-ing, Loit'ring
Rouse ye, then, O sleep-ers, Join the hap-py reap-ers; To the

sun-light, gold-en gleaming, Heav-ing like the rest-less main, "Reapers are
in the dust-y highways, Hear-ing not the Mas-ter say: "Reapers are
wind your sorrows flinging, Pa-tient-ly the sick-le wield: "Reapers are

Chorus.

need-ed," re-sounds o'er hill and plain.
need-ed, O who will work to-day?" Rouse ye then and to the fields a-
need-ed, A-wake, and to the field!

to the

way, Go la-bor for the Mas-ter while you may, Lo! He is calling,

field a-way, Mas-ter while you may,

Harvest Song.

night is fall-ing, Hast-en to o-bey, For reapers are needed to-day.

No. 89. Gethsemane.

Written by Dr. Scoville while at the Garden of Gethsemane in 1900.

Chas. Reign Scoville.   De Loss Smith.

1. There is a place to Christians dear, To Cal-v'ry's hill 'tis ver-y near;
2. When sorrow's heaviest, friends may sleep, Your aching heart the lone watch keep:
3. Then troub-led heart, do not de-spair, Tho' dark the night, come here in pray'r;
4. For joy that is be-fore you then, Go to your cross, de-spise its shame;

O suf-f'ring One, 'twas more to Thee, The gar-den of Geth-sem-a-ne.
When morning brings too much for thee, Your cup take to Geth-sem-a-ne.
For an-y task you'll strengthen'd be Thro' pray'r in our Geth-sem-a-ne.
In worlds un-end-ing you shall be Like Je-sus of Geth-sem-a-ne.

CHORUS.

O spot di-vine, so dear to me, Where Je-sus bled in ag-o-ny;

When bur-dens seem too great for thee, Go, friend, to your Geth-sem-a-ne.

Oh, it is Wonderful.

C. H. G.   Chas. H. Gabriel.

1. I stand all a - mazed at the love Je - sus of - fers me, Con - fused at the
2. I mar - vel that He would descend from His throne divine, To res - cue a
3. I think of His hands, pierc'd and bleeding to pay the debt! Such mercy, such

grace that so ful - ly He prof - fers me; I trem - ble to know that for
soul so re - bel-lious and proud as mine; That He should ex-tend His great
love and de - vo - tion can I for-get? No, no, I will praise and a -

rit.   rit.

me He was cru-ci-fied, That for me a sin-ner, He suffer'd, He bled and died.
love un - to such as I, Suf - fi-cient to own, to re-deem and to jus - ti - fy.
dore at the mer-cy-seat, Un - til at the glo-ri-fied throne I kneel at His feet.

CHORUS.

Oh, it is won - der - ful that He should care for me,
won - der - ful!

Oh, it is Wonderful.

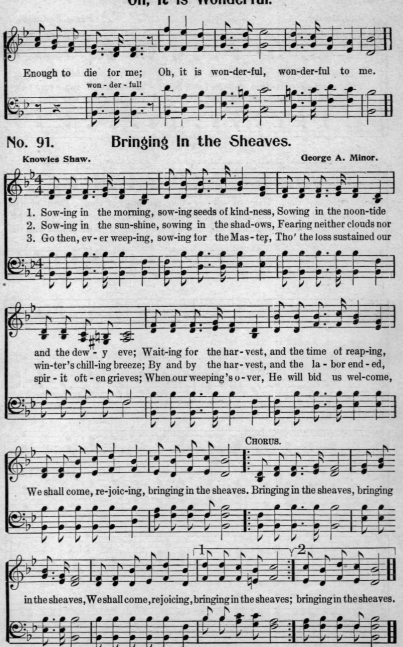

Enough to die for me; Oh, it is won-der-ful, won-der-ful to me.

won - der - ful!

No. 91. Bringing In the Sheaves.

Knowles Shaw.   George A. Minor.

1. Sow-ing in the morning, sow-ing seeds of kind-ness, Sowing in the noon-tide
2. Sow-ing in the sun-shine, sowing in the shad-ows, Fearing neither clouds nor
3. Go then, ev-er weep-ing, sow-ing for the Mas-ter, Tho' the loss sustained our

and the dew-y eve; Wait-ing for the har-vest, and the time of reap-ing,
win-ter's chill-ing breeze; By and by the har-vest, and the la-bor end-ed,
spir-it oft-en grieves; When our weeping's o-ver, He will bid us wel-come,

CHORUS.

We shall come, re-joic-ing, bringing in the sheaves. Bringing in the sheaves, bringing

in the sheaves, We shall come, rejoicing, bringing in the sheaves; bringing in the sheaves.

No. 92.   Blessed Assurance.

F. J. Crosby.   COPYRIGHT, 1873, BY JOS. F. KNAPP.   Mrs. J. F. Knapp.

1. Bless-ed as-sur-ance, Je-sus is mine! Oh, what a fore-taste of
2. Per-fect sub-mis-sion, per-fect de-light, Vis-ions of rap-ture now
3. Per-fect sub-mis-sion, all is at rest, I, in my Sav-ior am

glo-ry di-vine! Heir of sal-va-tion, purchase of God, Born of His
burst on my sight, An-gels de-scend-ing, bring from a-bove, Ech-oes of
hap-py and blest, Watching and wait-ing look-ing a-bove, Filled with His

Spir-it, washed in His blood.
mer-cy, whis-pers of love.   This is my sto-ry, This is my
good-ness, lost in His love.

song, Prais-ing my Sav-ior all the day long; This is my

sto-ry, this is my song; Prais-ing my Sav-ior all the day long.

No. 93.   I Am Happy in Him.

E. O. E.

E. O. Excell.

1. My soul is so hap-py in Je-sus, For He is so precious to me;
2. He sought me so long ere I knew Him, When wand'ring afar from the fold;
3. His love and His mer-cy surround me, His grace like a riv-er doth flow;
4. They say I shall some day be like Him, My cross and my burden lay down;

His voice it is music to hear it, His face it is heaven to see.
Safe home in His arms He hath bro't me, To where there are pleasures untold.
His Spir-it, to guide and to comfort, Is with me wher-ev-er I go.
Till then I will ev-er be faith-ful, In gath-er-ing gems for His crown.

CHORUS.

I am hap-py in Him, . . I am hap-py in Him; . .
I . . . . am hap-py in Him, I . . . . am hap-py in Him;

My soul with de-light He fills day and night, For I am hap-py in Him.

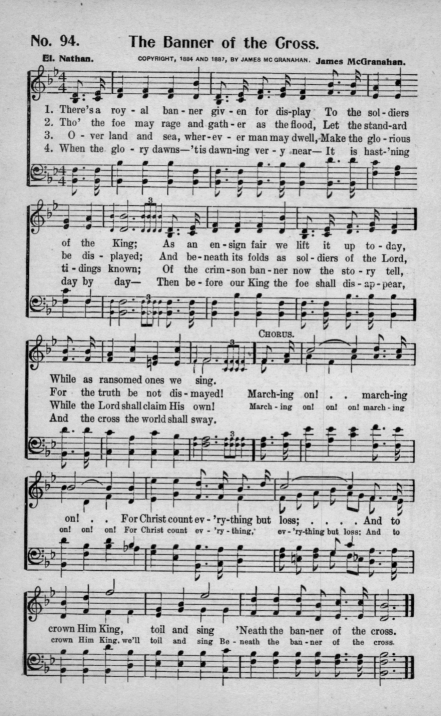

No. 94.

The Banner of the Cross.

El. Nathan.   COPYRIGHT, 1884 AND 1887, BY JAMES MC GRANAHAN.   James McGranahan.

1. There's a roy-al ban-ner giv-en for dis-play To the sol-diers
2. Tho' the foe may rage and gath-er as the flood, Let the stand-ard
3. O-ver land and sea, wher-ev-er man may dwell, Make the glo-rious
4. When the glo-ry dawns—'tis dawn-ing ver-y near— It is hast-'ning

of the King; As an en-sign fair we lift it up to-day,
be dis-played; And be-neath its folds as sol-diers of the Lord,
ti-dings known; Of the crim-son ban-ner now the sto-ry tell,
day by day— Then be-fore our King the foe shall dis-ap-pear,

CHORUS.

While as ransomed ones we sing.
For the truth be not dis-mayed!
While the Lord shall claim His own!
And the cross the world shall sway.

March-ing on! . . march-ing
March-ing on! on! on! march-ing

on! . . For Christ count ev-'ry-thing but loss; . . . . And to
on! on! on! For Christ count ev-'ry-thing, ev-'ry-thing but loss; And to

crown Him King, toil and sing 'Neath the ban-ner of the cross.
crown Him King, we'll toil and sing Be-neath the ban-ner of the cross.

Mother Knows.

Solo and Duet.

FROM WHITE RIBBON VIBRATIONS BY PER. ENGLEWOOD, COLO.

Anon. COPYRIGHT, 1890, BY FLORA H. CASSEL. Flora Hamilton Cassel.

1. No - bod - y knows of the work it makes To keep the home to-geth - er,
2. No - bod - y knows of the sleep-less care Bestowed on ba - by broth - er,
3. No - bod - y knows of the anxious fears, Lest darlings may not weath - er,
4. No - bod - y clings to the wayward child, Tho' scorn'd by ev - 'ry oth - er,

No - bod - y knows of the steps it takes, No - bod - y knows but moth - er;
No - bod - y knows of the tend - er pray'r, No - bod - y knows but moth - er;
Storms of this life in the com-ing years, No - bod - y knows but moth - er;
Leads it so gen tly from path-ways wild, No - bod - y can but moth - er;

No - bod - y list - ens to child-ish woes, Which kiss - es on - ly smoth - er,
No - bod - y knows of the lessons taught, Of lov - ing one an - oth - er;
No - bod - y knows of the tears that start, The grief she glad-ly smoth - er,
No - bod - y knows of the hour - ly pray'r, For him, our err - ing broth - er,

No - bod - y's pain'd by the might - y blow, No - bod - y,—on - ly moth - er.
No - bod - y knows of the patience sought, No - bod - y,—on - ly moth - er.
No - bod - y knows of the break-ing heart, No - bod - y,—on - ly moth - er.
Pride of her heart, once so pure and fair, No - bod - y,—on - ly moth - er.

No. 96. Loyalty to Christ.

Dr. E. T. Cassel.   Flora H. Cassel.

1. From o - ver hill and plain There comes the signal strain, 'Tis loy-al-ty, loy-al-ty,
2. O hear, ye brave, the sound That moves the earth around, 'Tis loy-al-ty, loy-al-ty,
3. Come, join our loy-al throng, We'll rout the giant wrong, 'Tis loy-al-ty, loy-al-ty,
4. The strength of youth we lay At Je - sus' feet to-day, 'Tis loy-al-ty, loy-al-ty,

loy-al-ty to Christ; Its mu - sic rolls a - long,   The hills take up the song,
loy-al-ty to Christ; A - rise to dare and do,   Ring out the watchword true,
loy-al-ty to Christ; Where Sa-tan's banners float We'll send the bu - gle note,
loy-al-ty to Christ; His gos - pel we'll proclaim Thro'-out the world's do-main,

CHORUS.

Of loy-al-ty, loy - al - ty, Yes, loy-al-ty to Christ. "On to vic-to-ry! On to

victory!" Cries our great Commander; "On!".... We'll move at His command,
great Commander; "On!"

We'll soon pos-sess the land, Thro' loy-al-ty, loy-al-ty, Yes, loy-al-ty to Christ.

No. 97. Keep the Heart Singing.

C. H. G.

COPYRIGHT 1902 BY CHAS. H. GABRIEL.
COPYRIGHT, 1907, BY E. O. EXCELL.

Chas. H. Gabriel.

1. We may light-en toil and care, Or a heav-y bur-den share, With a
2. If His love is in the soul, And we yield to His con-trol, Sweetest
3. How a word of love will cheer, Kin-dle hope, and ban-ish fear, Soothe a

word, a kind-ly deed, or sun-ny smile; We may gird-le day and night
mu-sic will the lone-ly hours be-guile; We may drive the clouds a-way,
pain, or take a-way the sting of guile; Oh, how much we all may do,

FINE.

With a ha-lo of de-light, If we keep the heart singing all the while.
Cheer and bless the darkest day, If we keep the heart singing all the while.
In the world we trav-el thro', If we keep the heart singing all the while.

CHORUS.

Keep the heart singing all the while; .... Make the world brighter with a
singing,   singing all the while;   brighter.

D. S.

smile; ...... Keep the song ringing! lone-ly hours we may be-guile,
brighter with a smile;

He Will Not Forsake You.

glo-ries shine a - far; He will not for-sake you Who numbers ev - 'ry star.

No. 99. Wonderful Words of Life.

P. P. B.

COPYRIGHT, 1905, BY THE JOHN CHURCH CO.
USED BY PERMISSION

P. P. Bliss.

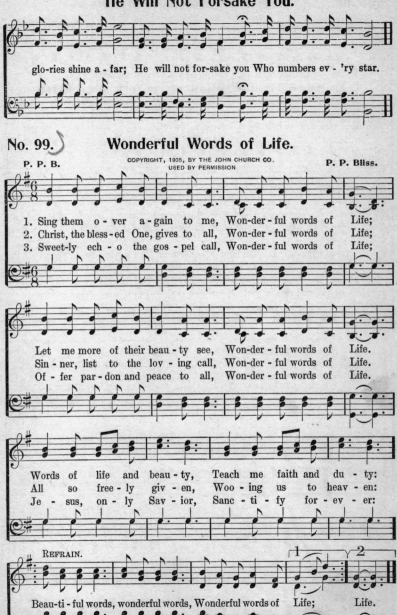

1. Sing them o - ver a - gain to me, Won-der - ful words of Life;
2. Christ, the bless - ed One, gives to all, Won-der - ful words of Life;
3. Sweet-ly ech - o the gos - pel call, Won-der - ful words of Life;

Let me more of their beau - ty see, Won-der - ful words of Life.
Sin - ner, list to the lov - ing call, Won-der - ful words of Life.
Of - fer par - don and peace to all, Won-der - ful words of Life.

Words of life and beau - ty, Teach me faith and du - ty:
All so free - ly giv - en, Woo - ing us to heav - en:
Je - sus, on - ly Sav - ior, Sanc - ti - fy for - ev - er:

REFRAIN.

Beau-ti - ful words, wonderful words, Wonderful words of Life; Life.

No. 100. Tell It Wherever You Go.

Rev. Johnson Oatman, Jr.

Wm. Edie Marks.

1. If Christ the Redeemer has pardoned your sin, Tell it wher-ev-er you go;
2. If now you are happy with Christ as your Guide, Tell it wher-ev-er you go;
3. When troubles as-sail do you trust in Him still? Tell it wher-ev-er you go;
4. If you are an heir to a man-sion on high, Tell it wher-ev-er you go;

If in-to your darkness His light has shown in Tell it wher-ev-er you go.
If He is your Friend, and with Him you a-bide, Tell it wher-ev-er you go.
When sorrows o'erwhelm do you sink in His will? Tell it wher-ev-er you go.
Un - til you find rest in that home in the sky, Tell it wher-ev-er you go.

CHORUS.

Tell it,....... tell it,....... Tell it wher-ev - er you go; If
Tell it that oth - ers a - round you may know,

you would win oth-ers fron sin and from woe, Tell it wher-ev-er you go!

No. 101. It is Well With My Soul.

H. G. Spafford.   P. P. Bliss.

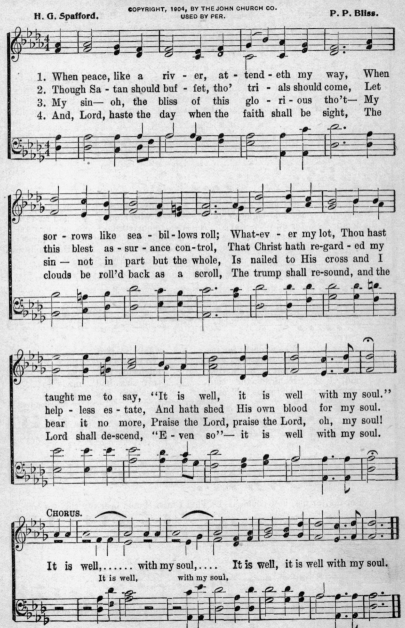

1. When peace, like a riv - er, at - tend - eth my way, When
2. Though Sa - tan should buf - fet, tho' tri - als should come, Let
3. My sin— oh, the bliss of this glo - ri - ous tho't— My
4. And, Lord, haste the day when the faith shall be sight, The

sor - rows like sea - bil - lows roll; What-ev - er my lot, Thou hast
this blest as - sur - ance con - trol, That Christ hath re-gard - ed my
sin — not in part but the whole, Is nailed to His cross and I
clouds be roll'd back as a scroll, The trump shall re-sound, and the

taught me to say, "It is well, it is well with my soul."
help - less es - tate, And hath shed His own blood for my soul.
bear it no more, Praise the Lord, praise the Lord, oh, my soul!
Lord shall de-scend, "E - ven so"— it is well with my soul.

CHORUS.

It is well,...... with my soul,.... It is well, it is well with my soul.

It is well,   with my soul,

No. 102.

All for Me.

Dr. E. T. Cassel.   E. T. and F. H. Cassel.

1. I look a - way,........ a-cross the sea,........ To Naz - er -
2. On mountains cold....... and des - erts bare........ His plead-ings
3. How oft up - on.......... His toil-some way...... He fought the
4. With-in the gar - den's deep-est shade...... In ag - o -
5. Be mine the crime,...... be mine the blame,..... That raised that

1. I look a-way,   a-cross the sea,

eth........ of Gal - i - lee,........ And there in faith..... my Lord I
pierce..... the mid-night air,...... A-lone with God...... and na-ture
temp - ter ev - 'ry day,...... And conquered sin...... in mor-tal
ny........ and gloom He pray'd,.. Where all my guilt...... on Him was
cru - el cross of shame,.... But let me sound...... His wondrous

To Nazareth   of Gal-i-lee,   And there in faith

see........ Who wrought for me........ sal - va-tion free........
there,...... He took my case........ to heav'n in pray'r......
clay,...... That I with Him........ might live for aye........
laid,...... He drank the cup........ my sins had made........
fame,...... And pub - lish ev - 'ry-where His name......

my Lord I see.   Who wrought for me,   salvation free.

CHORUS.

For me, for me, how could it be That Christ should bear my sins for me,

And suf - fer, oh, so cru - el - ly That I might live e - ter-nal - ly.

No. 103. The Two Lives.

James McGranahan.

Con espressione.

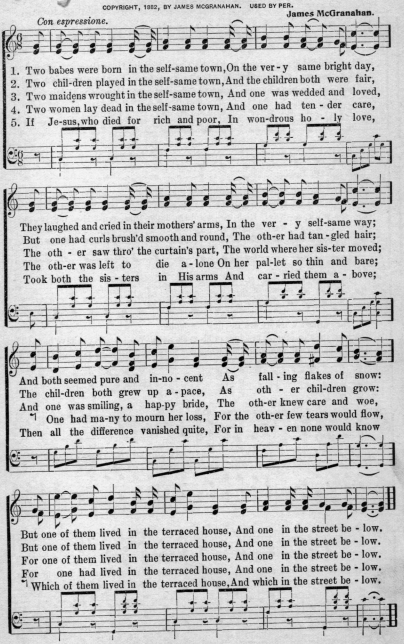

1. Two babes were born in the self-same town, On the ver-y same bright day,
2. Two chil-dren played in the self-same town, And the children both were fair,
3. Two maidens wrought in the self-same town, And one was wedded and loved,
4. Two women lay dead in the self-same town, And one had ten-der care,
5. If Je-sus, who died for rich and poor, In won-drous ho-ly love,

They laughed and cried in their mothers' arms, In the ver-y self-same way;
But one had curls brush'd smooth and round, The oth-er had tan-gled hair;
The oth-er saw thro' the curtain's part, The world where her sis-ter moved;
The oth-er was left to die a-lone On her pal-let so thin and bare;
Took both the sis-ters in His arms And car-ried them a-bove;

And both seemed pure and in-no-cent As fall-ing flakes of snow:
The chil-dren both grew up a-pace, As oth-er chil-dren grow:
And one was smiling, a hap-py bride, The oth-er knew care and woe,
One had ma-ny to mourn her loss, For the oth-er few tears would flow,
Then all the difference vanished quite, For in heav-en none would know

But one of them lived in the terraced house, And one in the street be-low.
But one of them lived in the terraced house, And one in the street be-low.
For one of them lived in the terraced house, And one in the street be-low.
For one had lived in the terraced house, And one in the street be-low.
Which of them lived in the terraced house, And which in the street be-low.

No. 104. Gathering for the King.

Mrs. N. P. C. Mrs. Nellie Place Chandler.

1. Har-vest fields are waving with the ripened grain, Hear the call, O reap-er!
2. Plen-te-ous the harvest, la-bor-ers are few; You have promis'd, worker,
3. Reap-er in life's harvest, hear the clar-ion call! Hast-en at His bid-ding

shall it be in vain! List-en! 'tis the Master, call-ing since the dawn;
will you not be true? Faith-ful to thy du-ty, think not of thine ease;
to the work, a-way! Rich re-ward He'll give thee, trust Him for it all;

O, for earnest workers, ere the day is gone.

CHORUS.

Gath-er for thy Master precious gold-en sheaves! We.........have heard Thee
Daylight soon will vanish, gather while you may. We have heard Thee call and

call-ing, Lord, In.........the field we'll glean for Thee; We will join the
faithful we will be; In the waving field we'll glean, O Lord, for Thee;

reapers as they work and sing, Gath-er-ing the harvest for the Lord, our King.

No. 105. There is Glory in My Soul.

Grace Weiser Davis.   Chas. H. Gabriel.

1. Since I lost my sins, and I found my Sav-ior There is glo-ry
2. Since He cleans'd my heart, gave me sight for blind-ness, There is glo-ry
3. Since with God I've walk'd, hav-ing sweet com-mun-ion, There is glo-ry
4. Since I en-ter'd Canaan on my way to heav-en, There is glo-ry

in my soul! Since by faith I sought and ob-tain'd God's fa-vor, There is
in my soul! Since He touch'd and heal'd me in lov-ing kind-ness, There is
in my soul! Brighter grows each day in this heav'n-ly un-ion, There is
in my soul! Since the day my life to the Lord was giv-en, There is

CHORUS.

glo-ry in my soul! There is glo-ry, glo-ry, there is glo-ry in my

soul! Ev-'ry day brighter grows, And I conquer all my foes; There is glo-ry,

glo-ry, there is glo-ry in my soul! There is glo-ry in my soul!
glo-ry in my soul!

The Grand Old Bible.

C. H. G.

Chas. H. Gabriel.

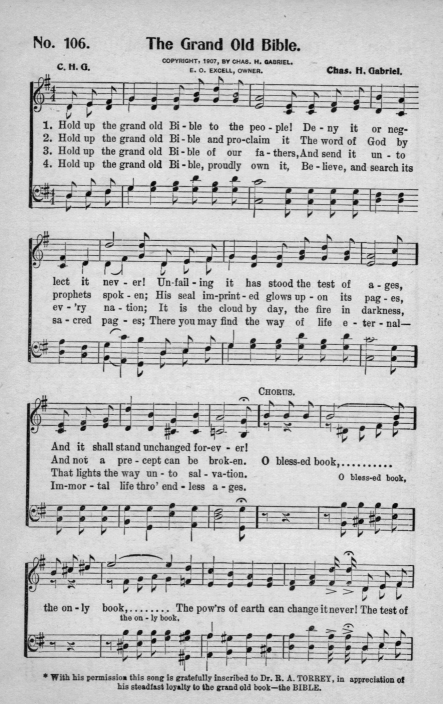

1. Hold up the grand old Bi-ble to the peo-ple! De-ny it or neg-
2. Hold up the grand old Bi-ble and pro-claim it The word of God by
3. Hold up the grand old Bi-ble of our fa-thers, And send it un-to
4. Hold up the grand old Bi-ble, proudly own it, Be-lieve, and search its

lect it nev-er! Un-fail-ing it has stood the test of a-ges,
prophets spok-en; His seal im-print-ed glows up-on its pag-es,
ev-'ry na-tion; It is the cloud by day, the fire in darkness,
sa-cred pag-es; There you may find the way of life e-ter-nal—

CHORUS.

And it shall stand unchanged for-ev-er!
And not a pre-cept can be brok-en. O bless-ed book,..........
That lights the way un-to sal-va-tion. O bless-ed book,
Im-mor-tal life thro' end-less a-ges.

the on-ly book,........ The pow'rs of earth can change it never! The test of
the on-ly book,

* With his permission this song is gratefully inscribed to Dr. R. A. TORREY, in appreciation of his steadfast loyalty to the grand old book—the BIBLE.

The Grand Old Bible.

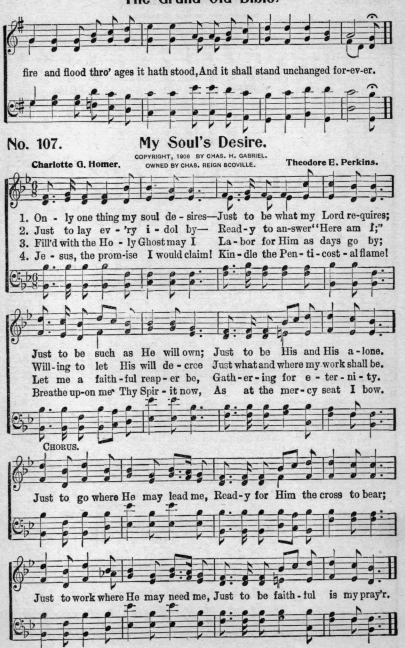

fire and flood thro' ages it hath stood, And it shall stand unchanged for-ev-er.

No. 107. My Soul's Desire.

Charlotte G. Homer.   Theodore E. Perkins.

1. On - ly one thing my soul de - sires—Just to be what my Lord re-quires;
2. Just to lay ev - 'ry i - dol by— Read-y to an-swer "Here am I;"
3. Fill'd with the Ho - ly Ghost may I La - bor for Him as days go by;
4. Je - sus, the prom-ise I would claim! Kin-dle the Pen - ti - cost - al flame!

Just to be such as He will own; Just to be His and His a - lone.
Will-ing to let His will de - cree Just what and where my work shall be.
Let me a faith-ful reap - er be, Gath-er-ing for e - ter - ni - ty.
Breathe up-on me Thy Spir - it now, As at the mer - cy seat I bow.

CHORUS.

Just to go where He may lead me, Read-y for Him the cross to bear;

Just to work where He may need me, Just to be faith - ful is my pray'r.

No. 108. A Wonderful Savior.

COPYRIGHT, 1907, BY CHAS. H. GABRIEL.
OWNED BY CHAS. REIGN SCOVILLE.

Mrs. Frank A. Breck.

Dr. W. H. Doane.

1. O have you not heard of a Sav-ior who came To die for a sin-ner like me? And have you been told of His won-der-ful name, And all that this Sav-ior will be? His name is called Je-sus! He saves us from sin, His love is far-reach-ing and true; He died on the cross, my sal-va-tion to win, And He is the Sav-ior for you.

2. The soul that is hun-gry He fills with good things; The thirst-y are ev-er sup-plied; The sor-row-ing spir-it tri-umph-ant-ly sings, When Je-sus is Shep-herd and Guide. O wan-der-er, come to this Sav-ior of men, He long-eth thy heart to re-new; To-day He is bring-ing sal-va-tion so near, And He is the Sav-ior for you.

3. Art wea-ry and faint-ing with fam-ine and strife? O come to Him just as you are, And ask for the bread and the wa-ter of life, And peace that no mor-tal can mar. In pen-i-tence low at His feet if you fall, Far more than you ask will He do; A won-der-ful Sav-ior is Je-sus for all, And He is the Sav-ior for you.

CHORUS.

O come to this

The Grand Old Bible.

fire and flood thro' ages it hath stood, And it shall stand unchanged for-ev-er.

No. 107.   My Soul's Desire.

Charlotte G. Homer.   **Theodore E. Perkins.**

1. On - ly one thing my soul de - sires—Just to be what my Lord re-quires;
2. Just to lay ev - 'ry i - dol by— Read-y to an-swer "Here am I;"
3. Fill'd with the Ho - ly Ghost may I   La-bor for Him as days go by;
4. Je - sus, the prom-ise I would claim! Kin-dle the Pen - ti - cost - al flame!

Just to be   such as He will own;   Just to be   His and His a - lone.
Will-ing to   let His will de - cree Just what and where my work shall be.
Let me a   faith-ful reap-er be,   Gath-er - ing for e - ter - ni - ty.
Breathe up-on me Thy Spir - it now, As   at the mer - cy seat I bow.

CHORUS.

Just to go where He may lead me, Read-y for Him the cross to bear;

Just to work where He may need me, Just to be faith-ful   is my pray'r.

No. 108.   A Wonderful Savior.

Mrs. Frank A. Breck.   **Dr. W. H. Doane.**

1. O have you not heard of a Sav-ior who came To die for a
2. The soul that is hun-gry He fills with good things; The thirst-y are
3. Art wea-ry and faint-ing with fam-ine and strife? O come to Him

sin-ner like me? And have you been told of His won-der-ful name, And
ev-er sup-plied; The sor-row-ing spir-it tri-umph-ant-ly sings, When
just as you are, And ask for the bread and the wa-ter of life, And

all that this Sav-ior will be? His name is called Je-sus! He saves us from
Je-sus is Shep-herd and Guide. O wan-der-er, come to this Sav-ior of
peace that no mor-tal can mar. In pen-i-tence low at His feet if you

sin, His love is far-reach-ing and true; He died on the cross, my sal-
men, He long-eth thy heart to re-new; To-day He is bring-ing sal-
fall, Far more than you ask will He do; A won-der-ful Sav-ior is

CHORUS.

va-tion to win, And He is the Sav-ior for you.
va-tion so near, And He is the Sav-ior for you. O come to this
Je-sus for all, And He is the Sav-ior for you.

A Wonderful Savior.

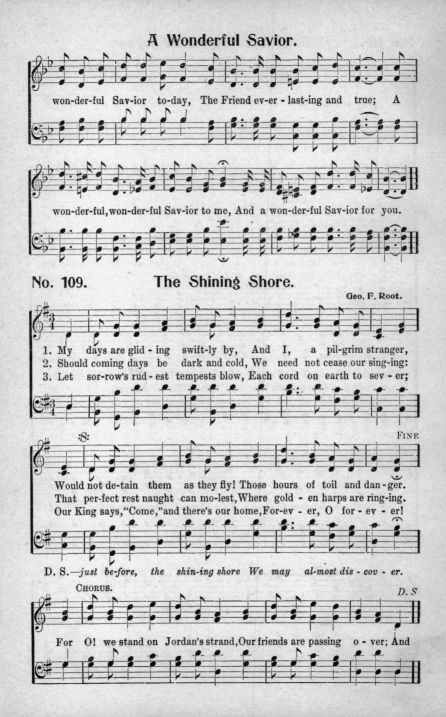

won-der-ful Sav-ior to-day, The Friend ev-er - last-ing and true; A

won-der-ful, won-der-ful Sav-ior to me, And a won-der-ful Sav-ior for you.

No. 109. The Shining Shore.

Geo. F. Root.

1. My days are glid - ing swift-ly by, And I, a pil-grim stranger,
2. Should coming days be dark and cold, We need not cease our sing-ing:
3. Let sor-row's rud - est tempests blow, Each cord on earth to sev - er;

FINE

Would not de-tain them as they fly! Those hours of toil and dan - ger.
That per-fect rest naught can mo-lest, Where gold - en harps are ring-ing.
Our King says, "Come," and there's our home, For-ev - er, O for - ev - er!

D. S.—*just be-fore, the shin-ing shore We may al-most dis - cov - er.*

CHORUS.

D. S

For O! we stand on Jordan's strand, Our friends are passing o - ver; And

No. 110. I Shall See My Savior's Face.

To Mrs. Princess Clark Long.

Chas. Reign Scoville.   COPYRIGHT, 1906, BY SCOVILLE & SMITH.   De Loss Smith.

1. I shall see my Sav-ior's face, When I reach that hap-py place Just be-
2. I shall see the nail pierc'd hand, When I reach the golden strand, 'Twill ex-
3. I shall see my moth-er's face, For she too was sav'd by grace, And with

yond the si-lent riv-er by and by; Oh, how hap-py I will be,
tend to me a wel-come by and by; I shall see the wound ed side,
Je-sus she will meet me by and by; With our lov'd ones we will be,

When His glo-ry I shall see, And I'll dwell with Him forev-er, by and by.
From which flow'd the crimson tide, And I'll praise Him for redemption, by and by.
There with Christ e-ter-nal-ly, No more parting at the riv-er by and by.

CHORUS

I shall see Him face to face, I shall know His boundless grace, When I

reach the Ho-ly Cit-y by and by; All my hopes I'll re-al-ize, In that

I Shall See My Savior's Face.

home be-yond the skies, When I see Him in His beau-ty by and by.

No. 111.

Lead Me, Savior.

F. M. D.

FROM "CAROLS OF JOY."
USED BY PERMISSION OF JOHN J. HOOD.

Frank M. Davis.

1. Sav - ior, lead me, lest I stray,   Gen - tly lead me all the way;
2. Thou the ref-uge of my soul   When life's stormy billows roll;
3. Sav - ior, lead me, then at last,   When the storm of life is past,

1. Sav - ior,   lead me, lest I stray, Gen - tly   lead me all the way;

I am safe when by Thy side,   I would in Thy love a - bide.
I am safe when Thou art nigh,   All my hopes on Thee re-ly.
To the land of end-less day,   Where all tears are wiped a-way.

I am   safe when by Thy side, I would   in Thy love abide.

CHORUS.

Lead me, lead me, Sav - ior, lead me, lest I stray; . .

lest I stray;

rit. e dim.

Gen-tly down the stream of time,   Lead me, Savior, all the way.

stream of time,   all the way.

No. 112. Bring Peace to My Soul.

Helen M. Dungan.

J. M. Dungan.

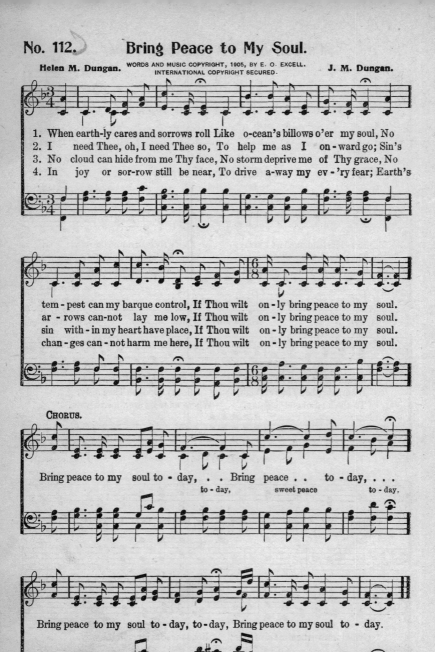

1. When earth-ly cares and sorrows roll Like o-cean's billows o'er my soul, No
2. I need Thee, oh, I need Thee so, To help me as I on-ward go; Sin's
3. No cloud can hide from me Thy face, No storm deprive me of Thy grace, No
4. In joy or sor-row still be near, To drive a-way my ev-'ry fear; Earth's

tem - pest can my barque control, If Thou wilt on - ly bring peace to my soul.
ar - rows can-not lay me low, If Thou wilt on - ly bring peace to my soul.
sin with - in my heart have place, If Thou wilt on - ly bring peace to my soul.
chan - ges can-not harm me here, If Thou wilt on - ly bring peace to my soul.

CHORUS.

Bring peace to my soul to - day, . . . Bring peace . . to - day, ...
to - day, sweet peace to - day,

Bring peace to my soul to - day, to - day, Bring peace to my soul to - day.

No. 113. Whom, Having Not Seen, I Love.

Maud Frazer.

Chas. H. Gabriel.

1. A Friend have I who standeth near, To com-fort me and still each fear;
2. In vain may fan-cy strive to trace My Sav-ior's beauty and His grace;
3. The pre-cious hope I have each day Il-lu-mines all my earth-ly way,
4. With that fair man-sion e'er in view, My pil-grim jour-ney I pur-sue,

It is my Lord and Sav-ior dear, Whom, hav-ing not seen, I love.
More fair than I can dream, His face, Whom, hav-ing not seen, I love.
That He will take me home to stay, Whom, hav-ing not seen, I love.
And try my Sav-ior's will to do, Whom, hav-ing not seen, I love.

CHORUS.

And He is pre-par-ing a place .... For me in His home a-bove, ...
And He is pre-par-ing a place For me in His home a-bove,

Where I shall be-hold His face, ... Whom, having not seen, I love.
Where I .... shall be-hold His face,

Because His Name is Jesus.

Arr. by E. O. E.

E. O. Excell.

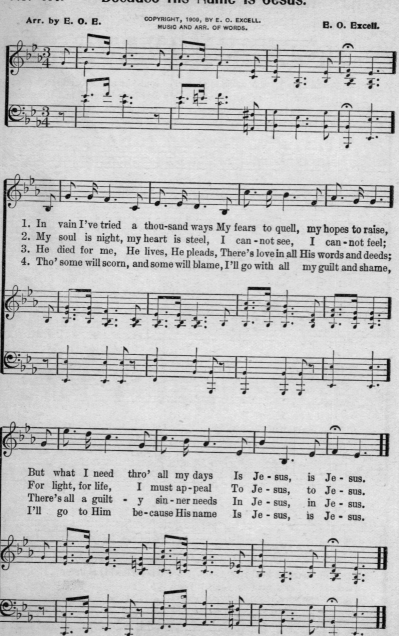

1. In vain I've tried a thou-sand ways My fears to quell, my hopes to raise,
2. My soul is night, my heart is steel, I can-not see, I can-not feel;
3. He died for me, He lives, He pleads, There's love in all His words and deeds;
4. Tho' some will scorn, and some will blame, I'll go with all my guilt and shame,

But what I need thro' all my days Is Je-sus, is Je-sus.
For light, for life, I must ap-peal To Je-sus, to Je-sus.
There's all a guilt-y sin-ner needs In Je-sus, in Je-sus.
I'll go to Him be-cause His name Is Je-sus, is Je-sus.

Special Choruses

No. 115.

Behold, I Stand at the Door.

F. M. D.

Frank M. Davis.

Be-hold, I stand at the door and knock, knock, knock, knock;

1. If an-y one .... will hear my voice, ... And o-pen wide ....
2. And shall I stand ... and knock in vain .... At thy heart's door, ..
3. O wear-y heart, ... O trem-bling soul, ... Un-do the door, ...

If an-y one   will hear my voice,   And o-pen wide

to me the door, ... I will come in .... and sup with him, .. And he with
O child of sin? .... I've waited long ... and patient-ly. ... Un-do the
long closed with sin; .. I bring you joy ... from heav'n above, And glad-ly

to me the door,   I will come in   and sup with him,

me ... for-ev-er-more, .. And he with me for-ev-er-more. ....
door .. and let me in, ... Un-do the door and let me in. .....
I .... would enter in, ... And glad-ly I would en-ter in. .....

And he with me   for-ev-er-more,   for-ev-er-more.

No. 116.   Christ is King.

COPYRIGHT, 1908, BY SCOVILLE & SMITH.
USED BY PER.

Chas. Reign Scoville.   De Loss Smith.

1. Come friends sing,   of the faith that's so dear to   me,
2. Cru - ci - fied,   thus He suf - fered and bled for   me,
3. At His feet,   on old Ol - i - vet's Hill they say,

Re - vealed thro' God's Son,   in Gai - i - lee;   He brought
Death and the grave won   sin's vic - to - ry;   Then the
Cloud char - iots halt - ed,   took Christ a - way;   Then the

peace on earth   and good will to the sons of   men,
sky grew dark   and the tem - ple veil rent in   twain,
an - gels came   and to wond'ring dis - ci - ples said

Go tell it to   the world, her King reigns a - gain.
Rocks rent, and an - gels came, for He lived a - gain.
He'll come, and earth and sea shall yield up their dead.

Christic is King.

CHORUS.

I am so hap-py in Je - sus, Cap-tiv-i-ty's Cap-tor is He; ... An - gels re-joice when a souls saved, Some day we like Him shall be, ... Sor-row and joy have the same Lord, Val-ley of shad-ows shall sing; ... Death has its life, its door o-pens in heav-en e-ter-nal-ly, Christ is King ....

cres.

Harmony.

Praise Ye the Father.

E. O. E.
Allegro Maestoso.

C. Gounod.

Introduction.

Praise ye the Father, let ev-'ry na-tion join to sing; Praise ye the Father, let ev-'ry heart its tribute bring, King ev-er-last-ing! The angels mag-ni-fy Thy name. King of all glo-ry? The worlds Thy might and pow'r proclaim. Praise ye the Lord, ev-'ry heart break forth and sing, For He is good .... un-to all, ... and His mercy is ev-er-last-ing.

O praise, our God break forth,

and sing. is good, to all, His mer-cy is ev-er-last-ing.

Praise Ye the Father.

He hath redeemed, and hath made us to be His children. By His death on the cross He
our. Lord,   re-deemed,   and made us   chil-dren,

ransom'd the world. Hallelujah! praise ye the Father. Glory be to the Father, to the

Son and to the Ho-ly Ghost, We sing glory, we sing glory, un-to Christ our Lord and

King,   Glo-ry un-to Christ our King. As it was in the beginning, is now, and
Hal-le-lu-jah!

ev-er shall be, world without end. A - men, A - men.   men, A - men.

No. 118. Victory.

Charlotte G. Homer.

Chas. H. Gabriel.

1. "Vic-to-ry!" is the song ech-o-ing loud and long From the redeemed of ev-'ry na-tion; Let the pae-an ring Of the conq'ring King Who hath brought so great sal-va-tion; Vic-to-ry in His name, Who a Re-deem-er came Un-to His own, to be re-ject-ed! Yet to day He

2. "Vic-to-ry!" o-ver sin, Pow-er and zeal to win Souls to the light from dark-ness drear-y Doth He free-ly give All who will receive, And the work is nev-er wea-ry; Vic-to-ry for the right, Patience to win the fight Faith-ful-ly day by day, He gives us; Our De-fence is

Victory.

lives, And a bless-ing gives, Tho' de-nied, re-viled, neg-lect - ed.
He, And will ev-er be Till in glo-ry He re-ceives us.

CHORUS.

Sing the sto - ry, Tell His glo - ry Un-til earth re-
Sing, O sing!   Sing, O sing!

ech-oes with His praise! Come be-fore Him! Laud, a-dore Him,
Sing, O sing!   Sing, sing!

1
Loud anthems of joy let us raise;

2
Loud an-thems of joy let us raise.

No. 119. Onward, Christian Soldiers!

To Prof. Chas. F. Allen.

Sabine Baring-Gould. COPYRIGHT, 1907, BY E. O. EXCELL. **E. O. Excell.**

1. On - ward, Chris-tian sol - diers! March-ing as to
2. At the sign of tri - umph Sa - tan's host doth
3. Like a might-y ar - my Moves the church of
4. On - ward, then, ye peo - ple! Join our hap - py

war, With the cross of Je - sus
flee; On, then, Chris - tian sol - diers,
God; Broth - ers, we are tread - ing
throng, Blend with ours your voic - es

Go - ing on be - fore. Christ, the roy - al
On to vic - to - ry! Hell's foun - da - tions
Where the saints have trod; We are not di -
In the tri - umph song; Glo - ry, laud, and

Onward, Christian Soldiers.

Mas - ter, Leads a - gainst the foe;............
quiv - er At the shout of praise;.........
vid - ed, All one bod - y we,............
hon - or Un - to Christ the King,..........

For-ward in - to bat - tle, See His ban - ners go!
Broth-ers, lift your voi - ces, Loud your an - thems raise.
One in hope and doc - trine, One in char - i - ty.
This thro' count-less a - ges Men and an - gels sing.

CHORUS.

Arthur S. Sullivan.

On-ward, Christian sol - diers! March-ing as to war, With the cross of

Je - sus Go - ing on be - fore. INTERLUDE.

No. 120. Jesus Reigns.

Chas. Reign Scoville. De Loss Smith.

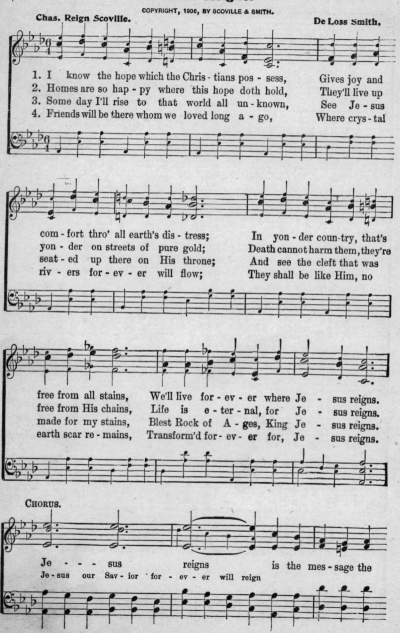

1. I know the hope which the Chris-tians pos-sess, Gives joy and
2. Homes are so hap-py where this hope doth hold, They'll live up
3. Some day I'll rise to that world all un-known, See Je-sus
4. Friends will be there whom we loved long a-go, Where crys-tal

com-fort thro' all earth's dis-tress; In yon-der coun-try, that's
yon-der on streets of pure gold; Death cannot harm them, they're
seat-ed up there on His throne; And see the cleft that was
riv-ers for-ev-er will flow; They shall be like Him, no

free from all stains, We'll live for-ev-er where Je - sus reigns.
free from His chains, Life is e-ter-nal, for Je - sus reigns.
made for my stains, Blest Rock of A-ges, King Je - sus reigns.
earth scar re-mains, Transform'd for-ev-er for, Je - sus reigns.

CHORUS.

Je - - - sus reigns is the mes-sage the
Je-sus our Sav-ior for - ev - er will reign

Jesus Reigns.

No. 121. The Tramp of the Host.

C. H. G.

Chas. H. Gabriel.

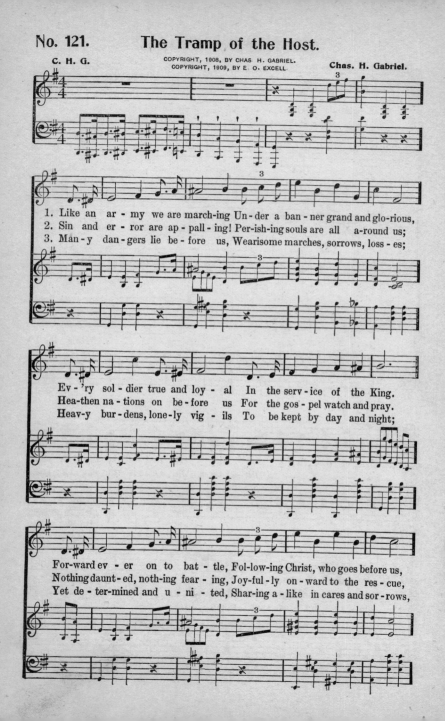

1. Like an ar - my we are march-ing Un - der a ban - ner grand and glo-rious,
2. Sin and er - ror are ap - pall - ing! Per-ish-ing souls are all a-round us;
3. Man - y dan - gers lie be - fore us, Wearisome marches, sorrows, loss - es;

Ev - 'ry sol - dier true and loy - al In the serv - ice of the King.
Hea-then na - tions on be - fore us For the gos - pel watch and pray.
Heav-y bur - dens, lone-ly vig - ils To be kept by day and night;

For-ward ev - er on to bat - tle, Fol-low-ing Christ, who goes before us,
Nothing daunt-ed, noth-ing fear - ing, Joy-ful-ly on-ward to the res - cue,
Yet de - ter-mined and u - ni - ted, Shar-ing a - like in cares and sor - rows,

The Tramp of the Host.

With a tramp, tramp, tramp, moving onward, While the victor's song we sing.
With a tramp, tramp, tramp, we are marching Where our Savior leads the way.
With a tramp, tramp, tramp, we are marching Upward to the land of light.

Chorus.

Like an ar - my with ban-ners fly - ing, A-gainst the hosts of sin we
March-ing on,   march-ing on,

march, march away! Souls in bond-age of sin are dy-ing; "They must and shall be
March-ing on,   march-ing on,

free!" "rings the war-cry to-day, "They must and shall be free!" "rings the war-cry to-day.

No. 122. Crown Him King of Kings.

E. E. Rexford.

DeLoss Smith.

INTRODUCTION.

VOICES IN UNISON.

1. Crown Him, crown Him with glo - ry the King of kings;
2. He who reigns o'er the king-doms of earth to - day,
3. Praise Him, praise Him, the King on the great white throne;

Praise and hom-age each heart as its trib - ute brings;
Sends His bless-ings to those in the heav'n - ward way;
Love Him, serve Him, who rul - eth by love a - lone;

Sing, O earth, and u - nite in the might - y re - frain—
Sing we prais-es with hearts that with love o - ver - flow—
Up to heav - en the shout of the glo - ri - fied rings—

Grown Him King of Kings.

Christ, our Re-deem-er and King, will for-ev-er reign!
Glo-ry to Je-sus who con-quers our ev-'ry foe!
Laud and a-dore Him, and crown Him the King of kings!

CHORUS.

Sing ho-san-nas, loud let the joy-ful an-thems ring,

Laud and wor-ship Him whom the an-gels a-dore!

Crown Him, crown Him, Sav-ior, Re-deem-er and King,

Glo-ry to God in the high-est— Glo-ry for-ev-er-more!

No. 123. Keep Up The Fight.

President Roosevelt to Spreckles, leader of the Reform Movement, San Francisco, Cal.,
"Keep up the Fight."

Eben E. Rexford.

Samuel W. Beazley.

Unison.

1. Keep up the fight! The bat-tle must be won, to-day God's or-der
2. Keep up the fight! The trum-pet's call rings far and wide; En-list to-
3. Keep up the fight Un-til the foe-men turn and fly; For Right we'll

is— Press on-ward to the fray! The hosts of sin your loy-al ranks must
day, Christ needs you on His side! For truth and right! Be this the cry, our
dare, and if it need be, die. The Truth must win, no mat-ter what the

put to rout, And from the land the foe be driv-en out.
ranks to lead, And God will give the cour-age that we need.
cost may be. Keep up the fight! God send us vic-to-ry!

Keep Up the Fight.

CHORUS.

Keep up the fight for Truth and Right! Led on by Christ we'll win the day. He goes be-fore us. His ban-ner o'er us To cer-tain vic-t'ry points the way. Keep up the fight and fal-ter nev-er; For right will live and reign for-ev-er; Our God is with us to cour-age give us, Keep up the fight, keep up the fight!

No. 124. Reapers for the Harvest.

Eben Rexford. Samuel W. Beasley.

1. Lo! all read - y for the gath-'ring God's great har - vest stands;
2. "Great the need but few have answered," hear the Mas - ter say;
3. O ye i - dlers join the cho - rus of the har - vest song,

Hark! the reap - ers' song is ring - ing up and down the lands;
From the work of loy - al serv - ice will you turn a - way?
Let its mu - sic rise to heav - en all the hills a - long;

Hear you not the call for work - men sound-ing o - ver hill and val-ley?
O for love of Christ who calls you to be reap - ers in His har-vest,
Those who reap God's grain and bind it, and go glean - ing in the by-ways,

An - swer quick - ly, bring to serv - ice will - ing hearts and hands.
An - swer "Mas - ter, I will glad - ly work for you to - day."
Find that work done for the Sav - ior makes the weak - est strong.

CHORUS.

Lo! the harvest ripe and read - y stands to-day; See, the

Lo! the har-vest ripe and read - y stands to - day, to - day; See the Mas-ter

Lo! the har - vest stand - ing read - y, See the

Reapers for the Harvest.

Master cometh, and He comes this way,   Seeking for reapers, let us

com - eth,   and He comes, He comes this way,

Mas - ter   comes   this   way;   He   seek - eth   reap - ers;

answer one and all,   For a great reward is offered if we heed His call.

quickly,

an - swer   quick - ly,

A-wake, a-wake,   the   harvest waits on ev - 'ry hill and plain;

See, the har-vest waits   on   ev - 'ry hill, on hill and plain;

See,   the   har - vest   waits   for   reap - ers;

Go,   and gath-er in the sheaves of golden grain;   Reap-ing and bind-ing

Go and gather in   the   sheaves of gold-en grain, quickly;

Go,   and   gath - er   for   the   Mas - ter;   Reap - ing,   bind-

rit.

ere the harvest pass a-way,   Answer quickly, "We will work to-day."

go ye,

ing   ere the harvest pass a - way,

No. 125. Marching in His Name.

Charlotte G. Homer.

Chas. H. Gabriel.

1. Like an ar - my we are mov - ing Stead - i - ly, and at com-mand,
2. Ma - ny foes concealed a - bout us, Would in-vade our ranks to - day,
3. In the light our ban - ner gleaming, Fills the heart with love and cheer,

Thro' a strange and hos - tile coun-try, To a bet - ter, bright-er land;
And with sub - tile ag - i - ta - tion, Seek to turn us from the way;
And the voice of our Re - deem - er, Qui - ets ev - 'ry doubt and fear;

Full e-quip'd, cour-age-ous, loy - al, With the gos - pel firm - ly shod,
But our Lead-er, on be - fore us, All their se - cret cun-ning knows,
Shoulder pressed to shoulder ev - er, With a tramp, tramp, tramp we move,

We are march-ing on to glo - ry, To the cit - y of our God.
And His wis - dom is for - ev - er Proof a-gainst the chief of foes.
On - ward, up - ward to the cit - y Built for us thro' Je - sus' love.

Marching in His Name.

CHORUS.

With a firm de-term-i-na-tion, And a trust that shall not wane,

For the King we have en-list-ed, And are march-ing in His train;

Our song of joy is ev-er ring-ing, while mov-ing up the great high-way

To a cit-y bright, e-ter-nal, In a land of cloud-less day,
land of cloud-less day,

To a cit-y bright e-ter-nal, In a land of cloud-less day.

The Song of Triumph.

Charlotte G. Homer.

Chas. H. Gabriel.

D. C.-1. We are march-ing un-der the ban-ner vic-to-rious;
2. God is with us, strong to sup-port and de-liv-er;
3. On-ward, on-ward! an-swer the call of the Lead-er;

Leav-ing all at the call of the Com-man-der we love;
In His might day and night stead-i-ly on-ward we move;
For the right we will fight, fear-less-ly en-ter the fray,

Tramp! tramp! Sa-tan's bat-tle-ments trem-ble be-fore us,
Where He leads, thro' val-ley, o'er mount-ain or riv-er,
Brave-ly, tru-ly heed-ing the sum-mons to serv-ice,

FINE.

"Vic-to-ry! vic-to-ry!" ech-o the courts a-bove!
We will go for we know in-fi-nite is His love.
Val-iant-ly, loy-al-ly bat-tle for Christ to-day.

The Song of Triumph.

No. 127. Fearless, I'll Follow.

Rev. James Lawson.   E. O. EXCELL, OWNER.   Fred H. Byshe.

Andante con espressivo. slowly.

1. I   will fol - low Thee my Sav - ior, Where-so-e'er my lot may be;
2. Tho' I meet with trib - u - la - tions, Sore-ly tempt-ed tho' I   be,

Melody ben marcato.

Where Thou go - est,   I will fol - low,   Yes, my Lord, I'll fol - low Thee.
I   re-mem - ber Thou wast tempted, And re - joice to fol - low Thee.

Tho' 'tis lone, and dark, and drear-y, Cheer - less tho' my   path may be,
Tho' to Jor-dan's roll - ing billows, Cold   and deep, Thou lead-est me.

Fearless, I'll Follow.

Con brio

If Thy voice I hear be - fore me, Fear-less - ly I'll fol - low Thee.
Thou hast crossed its waves be-fore me, And I still will fol - low Thee.

CHORUS. *Spiritoso*

I will fol - low Thee, my Savior; Thou didst shed Thy blood for me;
I will follow Thee, my Sav - ior; Thou didst shed Thy blood for me;

A tempo. *risoluto.*

And tho' all men should forsake Thee, By Thy grace I'll fol-low Thee.
And tho' all men should forsake Thee, By Thy pow'r and grace I'll fol-low Thee.

Rock of Ages,

A. M. Toplady.

COPYRIGHT, 1884, BY E. O. EXCELL

E. O. Excell.

1. Rock of A - ges cleft for me,
2. Could my tears for - ev - - er flow,
3. While I draw this fleet - - ing breath,

1. Rock of A - ges, cleft for me, Blest Rock of A - ges, cleft for me,
2. Could my tears for - ev - er flow, Oh! Could my tears for - ev - er flow,
3. While I draw this fleet-ing breath, Yes, While I draw this fleeting breath.

Let me hide my - self in Thee;
Could my zeal no lan - - guor know,
When mine eyes shall close in death,

Let me hide my - self in Thee, Oh! Let me hide my - self in Thee;
Could my zeal no languor know, Oh! Could my zeal no languor know,
When mine eyes shall close in death, Yes, When mine eyes shall close in death,

Let the wa - - ter and the blood,
These for sin could not a - tone,
When I rise to world's un - known,

Let the wa - ter and the blood, Oh! Let the wa - ter and the blood
These for sin could not a - tone, No, These for sin could not a - tone,
When I rise to world's un-known, Yes, When I rise to world's unknown,

Rock of Ages.

From Thy wound - ed side which flow'd,
Thou must save and Thou a - lone,
And be - hold Thee on Thy throne;

From Thy wound - ed side which flow'd, Yes, From Thy wound - ed side which flow'd,
Thou must save and Thou a - lone, Yes, Thou must save and Thou a - lone,
And be - hold Thee on Thy throne, Yes, And be - hold Thee on Thy throne,

rit.

Be of sin the doub - - le cure,
In my hand no price I bring;
Rock of A - ges, cleft for me,

rit.

Be of sin the doub - le cure, Yes, Be of sin the doub - le cure,
In my hand no price I bring, Lord, In my hand no price I bring,
Rock of A - ges, cleft for me, Blest Rock of A - ges, cleft for me,

Repeat pp

Save from wrath and make me pure.
Sim - ply to Thy cross I cling.
Let me hide my - self in Thee.

Repeat pp.

Save from wrath and make me pure, Yes, Save from wrath and make me pure.
Sim - ply to Thy cross I cling, Lord, Sim - ply to Thy cross I cling.
Let me hide my - self in Thee, Oh, Let me hide my - self in Thee.

His Love for Me.

F. M. Eastwood.

Fred H. Byshe.

1. You have heard of the sto-ry of Je - - - sus— Of His
2. You have heard how He blessed lit - tle chil - - - dren: "Come, all
3. You have heard how the blind, as they sought Him, Found their
4. You have heard how He spake to the tem - - - pest—How the

grace flow-ing bound-less and free, But there's no one can tell you the
ye that are wear - y," said He; So I came, and He gave me the
sight when He bade them to see; So my sin-blind-ed eyes have been
words "Peace, be still!" calmed the sea; So my soul found the peace that it

ful - ness Of His won-der-ful love for me. . . . .
bless - ing Of His won-der-ful love for me. . . . .
o - pened By His won-der-ful love for me. . . . .
longed for In His won-der-ful love for me. . . . .

CHORUS.

His love for me, His love for me! High as the heav'n, deep as the sea;

Love that will last thro' e - ter - ni - ty, His love for me, His love for me!

No. 130. In Thy Love.

Neal A. McAulay.   COPYRIGHT, 1889 BY E O. EXCELL.   E. O. Excell.

Unison.

1. Fa-ther, I am weak and sin-ful, Ev-er prone to go a-stray;
2. In the bil-lows of temp-ta-tion, When its waves are run-ning high,
3. Fa-ther, when the shades are fall-ing, And the night of death is near,
4. O-pen, then, the pearl-y por-tals, That un-wor-thy though I be,

Like a way-ward child of er-ror, I so oft-en lose my way.
Bear me o'er life's sea of troub-le, Leave me not to sink and die.
Guide me thro' the gloomy val-ley, With Thy light my jour-ney cheer.
I may join the ran-somed le-gions, There to dwell e-ter-nal-ly.

CHORUS.

In Thy love, O God, have mer-cy; In Thy grace re-deem my
In Thy love, O God, have mer-cy, In Thy grace re-

soul; Bring me back, O gentle Shepherd, keep me safe within Thy fold.
deem my soul; Bring me back,

No. 131.

He Will Hide Me.

WORDS AND MUSIC.

James Rowe.

E. O. Excell.

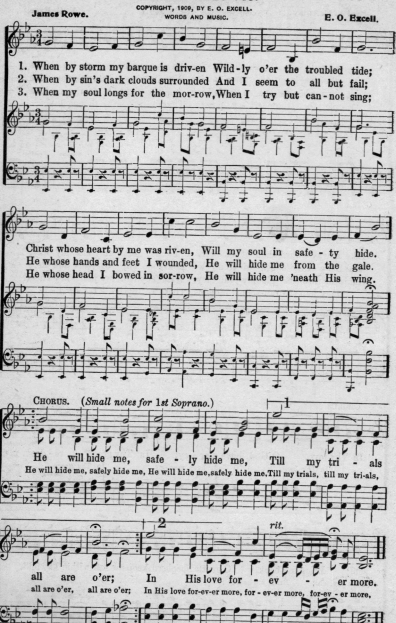

1. When by storm my barque is driv-en Wild-ly o'er the troubled tide;
2. When by sin's dark clouds surrounded And I seem to all but fail;
3. When my soul longs for the mor-row, When I try but can-not sing;

Christ whose heart by me was riv-en, Will my soul in safe-ty hide.
He whose hands and feet I wounded, He will hide me from the gale.
He whose head I bowed in sor-row, He will hide me 'neath His wing.

CHORUS. *(Small notes for 1st Soprano.)*

He will hide me, safe-ly hide me, Till my tri-als
He will hide me, safely hide me, He will hide me, safely hide me, Till my trials, till my tri-als,

all are o'er; In His love for-ev-er more.
all are o'er, all are o'er; In His love for-ev-er more, for-ev-er more, for-ev-er more,

rit.

Children's Songs

No. 132.

Dear Little Stranger.

C. H. G.

COPYRIGHT, 1900, BY E. O. EXCELL.
WORDS AND MUSIC.

Chas. H. Gabriel.

1. Low in a man - ger—dear lit - tle Stran - ger, Je - sus, the won - der - ful Savior, was born; There was none to receive Him, none to believe Him, None but the an - gels were watching that morn.

2. An - gels de-scend - ing, o - ver Him bend - ing, Chant-ed a ten - der and si - lent refrain; Then a won-der-ful sto - ry told of His glo - ry, Un - to the shepherds on Beth-le-hem's plain.

3. Dear lit - tle Stran - ger, born in a man - ger, Mak - er and Monarch, and Sav-ior of all; I will love Thee for-ev - er! grieve Thee? no, never! Thou didst for me make Thy bed in a stall.

CHORUS.

Dear lit - tle Stranger, slept in a man - ger,
But with the poor He slumbered se-cure, The

1.
2.

No down - y pil - low un - der His head; dear lit - tle Babe in His bed.

Little Sunbeams.

Eben E. Rexford,   Chas. H. Gabriel.

1. I think God gives the chil-dren, As thro' the land they go,
2. The clouds may hide the sun-shine Of heav-en from our sight,
3. Then let us live our mis-sion Of sun-beams day by day,

The most de-light-ful mis-sion That an-y one can know;
And life have much of sor-row To mar the heart's de-light;
And scat-ter joy and bright-ness A-bout us all the way;

He wants us to be sun-beams Of love, and hope, and cheer,
But if like faith-ful sun-beams, We chil-dren do our part,
Let's chase a-way life's shad-ows With lov-ing tho't and deed,

FINE.

To bright-en up the shad-ows That oft-en gath-er here.
We'll bring a ray of bright-ness To ev-'ry shadowed heart.
And be the sun-shine-mak-ers Of which the world has need.
D.S.—In all life's shad-y pla-ces We shine as best we can.

CHORUS.   D. S.

O we are lit-tle sun-beams, Sent down from God to man;

No. 134. The Sunday School Lighthouse.

Chas. Reign Scoville.

De Loss Smith.

1. The Sun-day School Lighthouse shines out on life's wave, It beams for all
2. The chan-nels are nar-row, sin's break-ers are there, Life's o-cean is
3. The work-ers are need-ed, the teach-ers are few, The Mas-ter, my
4. Where Un-be-lief's waves roll and storms are most fierce, The Sun-day School

na-tions, their chil-dren to save; Thro' Cal-va-ry's cross and thro'
strew'd with the wrecks of de-spair; Then build up, my broth-er, no
broth-er, de-pends up-on you; Don't wait for some wast-ed life
Lighthouse that dark gloom must pierce; 'Tis the gleam of that Star which at

Beth-le-hem's cave The light shines from glo-ry with pow-er to save.
time for de-lay, The Sunday School Lighthouse and save them to-day.
wreck'd on the shoals, The Sunday School Lighthouse must save lives and souls.
Beth-le-hem shone, The Sunday School Lighthouse will light the way home.

CHORUS.

Sunday School Lighthouse, Sunday School Lighthouse, Send out thy gleam o'er the wave;

Send thy gleam o'er the wave;

Sunday School Lighthouse, Sunday School Lighthouse, Help us the chil-dren to save.

No. 135. Open the Door for the Children.

Mary B. Kidder. COPYRIGHT, 1885, BY E. O. EXCELL. E. O. Excell.

1. O-pen the door for the chil-dren, Ten-der-ly gath-er them in,—
2. O-pen the door for the chil-dren, See, they are com-ing in throngs!
3. O-pen the door for the chil-dren, Take the dear lambs by the hand;

In from the high-ways and hedg-es, In from the plac-es of sin;
Bid them sit down to the ban-quet, Teach them your beau-ti-ful songs;
Point them to truth and to good-ness, Lead them to Ca-naan's fair land.

Some are so young and so help-less, Some are so hun-gry and cold;
Pray for the Fa-ther to bless them, Pray you that grace may be giv'n;
Some are so young and so help-less, Some are so hun-gry and cold;

D. S.—O-pen the door for the chil-dren, Gath-er them in-to the fold.
O-pen the door for the chil-dren, Theirs is the king-dom of heav'n.
O-pen the door for the chil-dren, Gath-er them in-to the fold.

FINE.

CHORUS. D. S.

O - pen the door, . . . Gath - er them in, . . .
O-pen the door, o-pen the door, Gath-er them in, gath-er them in,

No. 136.
I'll Be a Sunbeam.

To my grandson, Edwin O. Excell, Jr.

Nellie Talbot.

E. O. Excell.

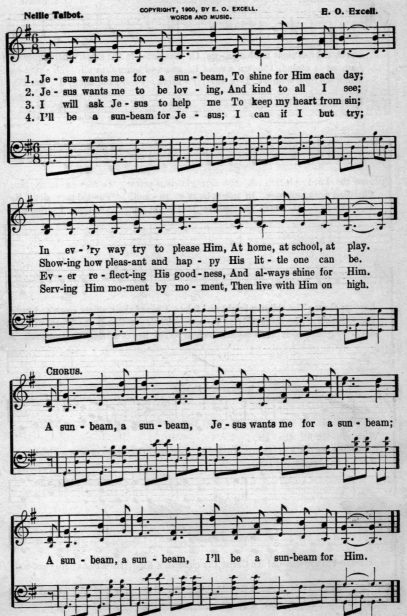

1. Je-sus wants me for a sun-beam, To shine for Him each day;
2. Je-sus wants me to be lov-ing, And kind to all I see;
3. I will ask Je-sus to help me To keep my heart from sin;
4. I'll be a sun-beam for Je-sus; I can if I but try;

In ev-'ry way try to please Him, At home, at school, at play.
Show-ing how pleas-ant and hap-py His lit-tle one can be.
Ev-er re-flect-ing His good-ness, And al-ways shine for Him.
Serv-ing Him mo-ment by mo-ment, Then live with Him on high.

CHORUS.

A sun-beam, a sun-beam, Je-sus wants me for a sun-beam;

A sun-beam, a sun-beam, I'll be a sun-beam for Him.

No. 137.   The Children's Hosanna.

Neal A. McAuley   J. S. Fearis.

1. I dreamed one night, not long a-go, Of mansions in the skies, Where those who love the Lord ob-tain A rich and glo-rious prize; I saw a-mong the hap-py throng The children bright and fair; I heard their voices clear and sweet With mu-sic fill the air.

2. And, as I mused, I heard a voice, In sweet-er tones than all, Di-rect-ing Christian work-ers here, In words I now re-call, "For-bid them not," He gen-tly said, "The children bring to me, Their por-tion in the World of Light Redeemed shall ev-er be."

3. And when from slumber I a-rose, To serve my Lord and King, I felt that I the lit-tle lambs To Christ in love might bring; And then I cried for dai-ly grace Their precious souls to cheer, Till they could sing like yonder choir Ho-san-na! bright and clear.

REFRAIN. *Faster.*

Hosanna! Hosanna! Our songs of love we bring, we bring Ho-san-na! Ho-san-na! To Christ, the children's King; Ho-san-na! Ho-san-na!

The Children's Hosanna.

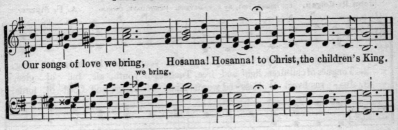

Our songs of love we bring, Hosanna! Hosanna! to Christ, the children's King.
we bring.

No. 138.

Onward, Little Soldiers!

James Rowe.

COPYRIGHT, 1902, BY CHAS. H. GABRIEL.
E O. EXCELL, OWNER.

Martin A. Elliott.

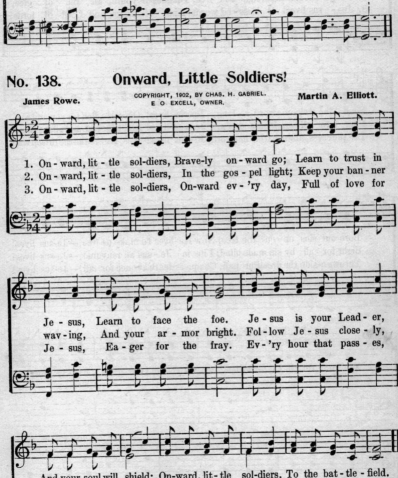

1. On - ward, lit - tle sol-diers, Brave-ly on - ward go; Learn to trust in
2. On - ward, lit - tle sol-diers, In the gos - pel light; Keep your ban - ner
3. On - ward, lit - tle sol-diers, On-ward ev - 'ry day, Full of love for

Je - sus, Learn to face the foe. Je - sus is your Lead - er,
wav - ing, And your ar - mor bright. Fol-low Je - sus close - ly,
Je - sus, Ea - ger for the fray. Ev - 'ry hour that pass - es,

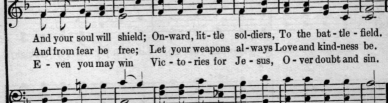

And your soul will shield; On-ward, lit - tle sol-diers, To the bat - tle - field.
And from fear be free; Let your weapons al - ways Love and kind-ness be.
E - ven you may win Vic - to - ries for Je - sus, O - ver doubt and sin.

No. 139. Mighty Army of the Young.

John R. Colgan. COPYRIGHT, 1891, BY A. F. MEYERS. HENRY DATE, OWNER. A. F. Myers.

1. Might-y ar-my of the young, Lift your voice in cheer-ful song,
2. Tongues of chil-dren, light and free, Tongues of youth, all full of glee,
3. Je - sus lives! O bless-ed words! King of kings, and Lord of lords!

Send the welcome word a-long, Je-sus lives! Once He died for you and me,
Sing to all on land and sea, Je-sus lives! Light for you, and all mankind,
Lift the cross, and sheathe the sword, Je-sus lives! See, He breaks the prison wall,

Bore our sins up-on the tree; Now He lives to make us free,—Je-sus lives!
Sight for all by sin made blind; Life in Je - sus all may find,—Je-sus lives!
Throws a-side the dreadful pall, Conquers death at once for all,—Je-sus lives!

CHORUS.

Wait not till the shad-ows lengthen, till you old-er grow, Ral-ly now, and
Wait not,

Wait not, wait not, Sing for

sing for Je-sus ev-'ry-where you go; Lift your joy-ful voi-ces high,
Sing,

Je - sus,

Mighty Army of the Young.

Repeat Chorus pp.
f rit.

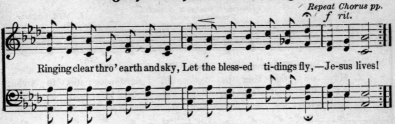

Ringing clear thro' earth and sky, Let the bless-ed ti-dings fly,—Je-sus lives!

No. 140. Savior, Like a Shepherd.

Dorothy A. Thrupp.   William B. Bradbury.

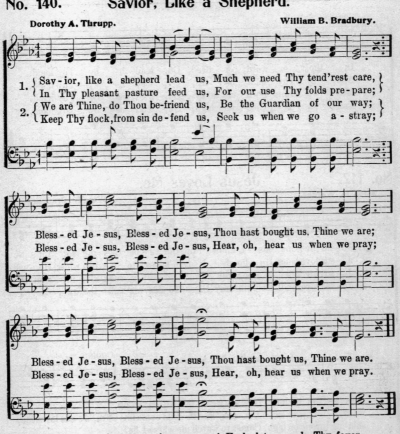

1. { Sav-ior, like a shepherd lead us, Much we need Thy tend'rest care, }
   { In Thy pleasant pasture feed us, For our use Thy folds pre-pare; }

2. { We are Thine, do Thou be-friend us, Be the Guardian of our way; }
   { Keep Thy flock, from sin de-fend us, Seek us when we go a - stray; }

Bless - ed Je - sus, Bless - ed Je - sus, Thou hast bought us, Thine we are;

Bless - ed Je - sus, Bless - ed Je - sus, Hear, oh, hear us when we pray;

Bless - ed Je - sus, Bless - ed Je - sus, Thou hast bought us, Thine we are.

Bless - ed Je - sus, Bless - ed Je - sus, Hear, oh, hear us when we pray.

3 Thou hast promised to receive us,
    Poor and sinful though we be;
Thou hast mercy to relieve us;
    Grace to cleanse and power to free;
      Blessed Jesus,
We will early turn to Thee.

4 Early let us seek Thy favor,
    Early let us do Thy will;
Blessed Lord and only Savior,
    With Thy love our bosoms fill;
      Blessed Jesus,
Thou hast loved us, love us still.

No. 141.

Lead Us By Thy Hand.

J. M. D.

J. M. Dungan.

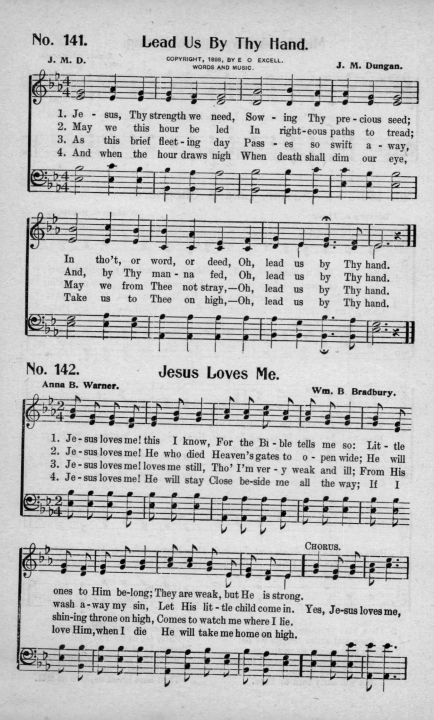

1. Je - sus, Thy strength we need, Sow - ing Thy pre - cious seed;
2. May we this hour be led In right-eous paths to tread;
3. As this brief fleet - ing day Pass - es so swift a - way,
4. And when the hour draws nigh When death shall dim our eye,

In tho't, or word, or deed, Oh, lead us by Thy hand.
And, by Thy man - na fed, Oh, lead us by Thy hand.
May we from Thee not stray,—Oh, lead us by Thy hand.
Take us to Thee on high,—Oh, lead us by Thy hand.

No. 142.

Jesus Loves Me.

Anna B. Warner.

Wm. B Bradbury.

1. Je - sus loves me! this I know, For the Bi - ble tells me so: Lit - tle
2. Je - sus loves me! He who died Heaven's gates to o - pen wide; He will
3. Je - sus loves me! loves me still, Tho' I'm ver - y weak and ill; From His
4. Je - sus loves me! He will stay Close be-side me all the way; If I

CHORUS.

ones to Him be-long; They are weak, but He is strong.
wash a-way my sin, Let His lit - tle child come in. Yes, Je-sus loves me,
shin-ing throne on high, Comes to watch me where I lie.
love Him, when I die He will take me home on high.

Jesus Loves Me.

Yes, Je-sus loves me, Yes, Je-sus loves me, The Bi-ble tells me so.

No. 143. Raindrops of Mercy.

Laura M. Moore.

COPYRIGHT, 1905, BY DE LOSS SMITH.

De Loss Smith.

1. We are God's dear little rain-drops Wait-ing to serve Him to-day;
2. Je-sus forgets not His rain-drops, For He has number'd them all;
3. It is God's wish that His rain-drops Out in the parch'd world should go;
4. We would do something for Je-sus, Showing that our love is true,

Singing His glad songs of prais-es, Learning to watch and to pray.
Just as God knoweth the spar-rows, Griev-ing if a-ny doth fall.
Scatter-ing blessings of mer-cy, That all His goodness may know.
So we will love one an-oth-er, As He has told us to do.

CHORUS.

Rain-drops, glad rain-drops of mer-cy, Sent from the fountain a-bove;

Rain-drops, glad raindrops of mer-cy, Fill'd with the light of God's love.

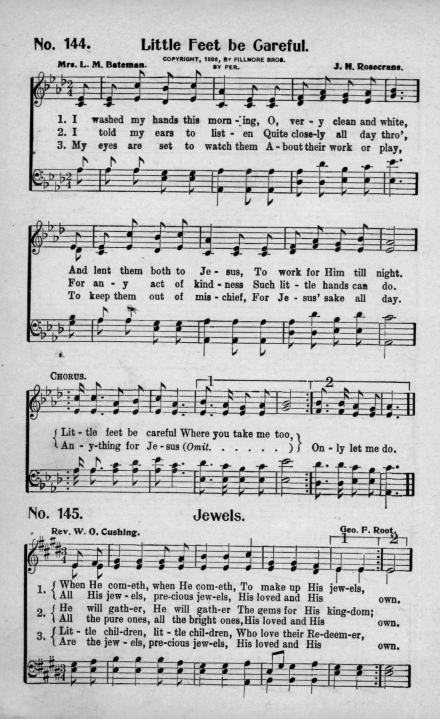

No. 144. Little Feet be Careful.

COPYRIGHT, 1886, BY FILLMORE BROS.
BY PER.

Mrs. L. M. Bateman.

J. H. Rosecrans.

1. I washed my hands this morn-ing, O, ver-y clean and white,
2. I told my ears to list-en Quite close-ly all day thro',
3. My eyes are set to watch them A-bout their work or play,

And lent them both to Je-sus, To work for Him till night.
For an-y act of kind-ness Such lit-tle hands can do.
To keep them out of mis-chief, For Je-sus' sake all day.

CHORUS.

{ Lit-tle feet be careful Where you take me too,
{ An-y-thing for Je-sus (Omit. . . . . .) } On-ly let me do.

No. 145. Jewels.

Rev. W. O. Cushing.

Geo. F. Root.

1. { When He com-eth, when He com-eth, To make up His jew-els,
   { All His jew-els, pre-cious jew-els, His loved and His own.

2. { He will gath-er, He will gath-er The gems for His king-dom;
   { All the pure ones, all the bright ones, His loved and His own.

3. { Lit-tle chil-dren, lit-tle chil-dren, Who love their Re-deem-er,
   { Are the jew-els, pre-cious jew-els, His loved and His own.

Jewels.

{ Like the stars of the morning, His bright crown adorning,
{ They shall shine in their beauty (*Omit* . . . .) Bright gems for His crown.

No. 146.

Love Song.

Sadie M. Thomas.   COPYRIGHT, 1903, BY THE HEIDELBERG PRESS.   Emory L. Coblentz.

1. Hap - py lit - tle chil - dren, Hap - py all day long, Do you know the
2. Jew - els for the crown-ing Of our bless - ed King; Hap - py lit - tle
3. Hap - py lit - tle chil - dren On this Ho - ly day; Would you know the
4. Love came down from heav-en Long, long, time a - go; Do you then need

REFRAIN.

se - cret Of our hap - py song?
chil - dren, Joy-ous - ly we sing.   L O V E, love,   L O
rea - son, List - en what we say.
won - der Why we love Him so?

V E, love,   This is why we are so hap-py;   L O V E, love.

Sunday-School Cadets.

C. B. A.

Mrs. Carrie B. Adams.

1. { We're ca - dets that want to bat - tle for the right, you see;
   { For our watch-word we have cho - sen "Hon - or bright!" you see,

2. { We're de - ter-mined that we'll nev - er know de - feat, you see,
   { For our Lead - er nev - er taught us to re - treat, you see,

That is why we band ourselves to - gether; And we'll keep it up in
If we fight for right, we'll win the bat - tle; No mat-ter how the

ev - 'ry kind of weather. For the right, then; Hon - or bright, then;
guns and sa-bers rat-tle. We'll be strong, then, 'Gainst the wrong, then,

We will march on our jour-ney thro' the world; Col-ors fly - ing,
And we'll work till the set - ting of the sun; Col-ors fly - ing,

Ev - er try - ing To be true, as our ban-ner is un - furled.
Ev - er try - ing To be faith - ful un - til the vict'ry's won.

Sunday-School Cadets.

CHORUS.

{ Then see us march-ing as to war, With purpose steady, Our hearts are
{ Our gallant Lead-er goes be- [Omit]

read-y; fore; Then see us march! We're the Sunday-School cadets!

No. 148. Bring Them In.

Alexcenah Thomas.

W. A. Ogden.

1. Hark! 'tis the Shepherd's voice I hear, Out in the des - ert dark and drear,
2. Who'll go and help this Shepherd kind, Help Him the wand'ring ones to find?
3. Out in the des - ert hear their cry, Out on the mountains wild and high,

Call - ing the sheep who've gone a-stray Far from the Shepherd's fold a - way.
Who'll bring the lost ones to the fold, Where they'll be sheltered from the cold?
Hark! 'tis the Mas - ter speaks to thee, "Go find my sheep wher-e'er they be."

CHORUS.

{ Bring them in, Bring them in, Bring them in from the fields of sin; }
{ Bring them in, Bring them in, Bring the wand'ring ones to } Je - sus.

Jesus Bids Us Shine.

E. O. Excell.

1. Je - sus bids us shine, With a clear, pure light, Like a lit - tle
2. Je - sus bids us shine, First of all for Him; Well He sees and
3. Je - sus bids us shine, Then for all a - round, Ma - ny kinds of
4. Je - sus bids us shine, As we work for Him, Bring - ing those that

can - dle Burn - ing in the night; In this world of dark - ness,
knows it If our light is dim; He looks down from heav - en,
dark - ness In this world a - bound, Sin and want and sor - row;
wan - der From the paths of sin; He will ev - er help us,

We must shine, You in your small cor - ner, And I in mine.
Sees us shine, You in your small cor - ner, And I in mine.
We must shine, You in your small cor - ner, And I in mine.
If we shine, You in your small cor - ner, And I in mine.

No. 150. **Hear Our Prayer.**

Anon.

John Adcock.

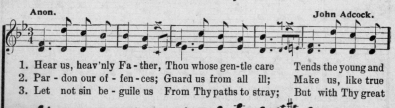

1. Hear us, heav'nly Fa - ther, Thou whose gen - tle care   Tends the young and
2. Par - don our of - fen - ces; Guard us from all ill;   Make us, like true
3. Let not sin be - guile us From Thy paths to stray;   But with Thy great

Hear Our Prayer.

fee - ble,— Hear our sim-ple prayer! Hear our prayer! Fa - ther, hear!
chil - dren, Love Thy ho - ly will. Hear our prayer! Fa - ther, hear!
mer - cy Keep us night and day. Hear our prayer! Fa - ther, hear!

No. 151. Somebody.

John R. Clements.

W. S. Weeden.

1. Somebody did a gold-en deed, Prov-ing him-self a friend in need;
2. Somebody tho't 'tis sweet to live, Will-ing - ly said, "I'm glad to give;"
3. Somebody i - dled all the hours, Care-less-ly crush'd life's fairest flow'rs,
4. Somebody fill'd the day with light, Constantly chased a - way the night;

Somebody sang a cheerful song. Bright'ning the skies the whole day long,—
Somebody fought a val-iant fight, Bravely he lived to shield the right,—
Somebody made life loss, not gain, Tho'tlessly seemed to live in vain,—
Somebody's work bore joy and peace, Sure-ly his life shall nev-er cease,—

rit.

Was that some-bod - y you? Was that some-bod - y you?

No. 152.

Little Stars.

H. H. Pierson.

J. S. Fearis.

1. Just as the stars are shin - ing, Mak - ing the dark - ness bright,
2. And as the stars are smil - ing, Down on the earth be - low,
3. Each in his lit - tle cor - ner, Wheth-er at work or play,
4. How could they do with - out us? Dark would the world be then;

So we are shin - ing, shin - ing, Shed-ding our gold - en light.
We may re - flect the sun-light, Shin - ing wher - e'er we go.
We would be al - ways shin - ing, Turn - ing the night to day.
We are the Sav - ior's jew - els, Cheer - ing the hearts of men.

CHORUS.

Shin - ing, shin - ing, shin - ing, Just like the stars a - bove,

Mak - ing the world a - round us, Hap - py with light and love.

No. 153. All Hail the Power of Jesus' Name.

Edward Perronet.

Oliver Holden.

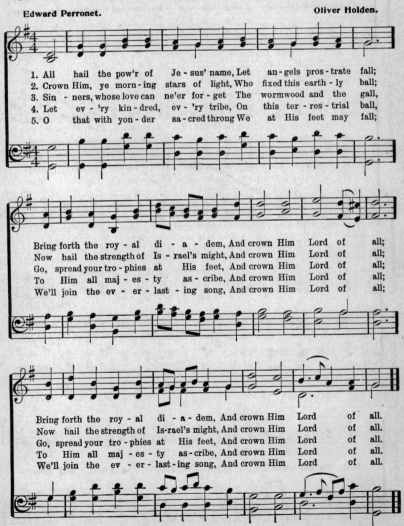

1. All hail the pow'r of Je - sus' name, Let an - gels pros - trate fall;
2. Crown Him, ye morn - ing stars of light, Who fixed this earth - ly ball;
3. Sin - ners, whose love can ne'er for - get The wormwood and the gall,
4. Let ev - 'ry kin - dred, ev - 'ry tribe, On this ter - res - trial ball,
5. O that with yon - der sa - cred throng We at His feet may fall;

Bring forth the roy - al di - a - dem, And crown Him Lord of all;
Now hail the strength of Is - rael's might, And crown Him Lord of all;
Go, spread your tro - phies at His feet, And crown Him Lord of all;
To Him all maj - es - ty as - cribe, And crown Him Lord of all;
We'll join the ev - er - last - ing song, And crown Him Lord of all;

Bring forth the roy - al di - a - dem, And crown Him Lord of all.
Now hail the strength of Is - rael's might, And crown Him Lord of all.
Go, spread your tro - phies at His feet, And crown Him Lord of all.
To Him all maj - es - ty as - cribe, And crown Him Lord of all.
We'll join the ev - er - last - ing song, And crown Him Lord of all.

No. 154. The Master's Call.

Chas. Reign Scoville,

De Loss Smith,

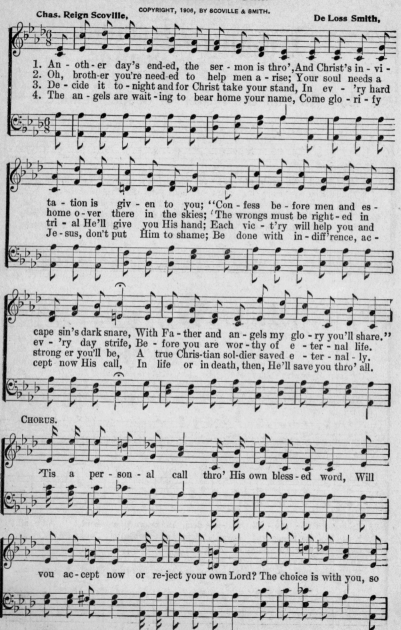

1. An - oth - er day's end - ed, the ser - mon is thro', And Christ's in - vi -
2. Oh, broth - er you're need - ed to help men a - rise; Your soul needs a
3. De - cide it to - night and for Christ take your stand, In ev - 'ry hard
4. The an - gels are wait - ing to bear home your name, Come glo - ri - fy

ta - tion is giv - en to you; "Con - fess be - fore men and es -
home o - ver there in the skies; 'The wrongs must be right - ed in
tri - al He'll give you His hand; Each vic - t'ry will help you and
Je - sus, don't put Him to shame; Be done with in - diff'rence, ac -

cape sin's dark snare, With Fa - ther and an - gels my glo - ry you'll share."
ev - 'ry day strife, Be - fore you are wor - thy of e - ter - nal life.
strong er you'll be, A true Chris - tian sol - dier saved e - ter - nal - ly.
cept now His call, In life or in death, then, He'll save you thro' all.

CHORUS.

'Tis a per - son - al call thro' His own bless - ed word, Will

you ac - cept now or re - ject your own Lord? The choice is with you, so

The Master's Call.

do not de - lay, As you an - swer Him now, He will an - swer that day.

No. 155.   He is the Savior You Need.

L. E. J.   L. E. Jones.

1. Have you ac - cept - ed of Je - sus, the Lord? He is the Sav - ior you need!
2. He will support you when tempted and tried, He is the Sav - ior you need;
3. He will de - liv - er thee out of de - spair, He is the Sav - ior you need;
4. Trust Him, believe Him, accept and o - bey, He is the Sav - ior you need;

Do you be - lieve Him and trust in His word? He is the Sav - ior you need.
He will be near you to guard and to guide, He is the Sav - ior you need.
He all your burdens and sorrows will share, He is the Sav - ior you need.
Doubting no long - er, re - ceive Him to - day, He is the Sav - ior you need.

CHORUS.

He . . is the Sav - ior you need, He . . is a Sav - ior in - deed;
He is the Sav - ior,   He is a Sav - ior,

Cru - ci - fied One, God's well be - loved Son, He is the Sav - ior you need.

No. 156. Softly and Tenderly.

BY PER. WILL L. THOMPSON & CO., E. LIVERPOOL, O·, AND THE THOMPSON MUSIC CO., CHICAGO, ILL.

W. L. T.

Will L. Thompson.

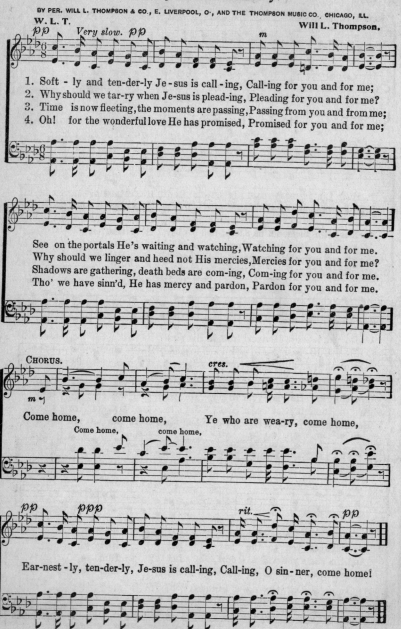

1. Soft - ly and ten-der-ly Je-sus is call-ing, Call-ing for you and for me;
2. Why should we tar-ry when Je-sus is plead-ing, Pleading for you and for me?
3. Time is now fleeting, the moments are passing, Passing from you and from me;
4. Oh! for the wonderful love He has promised, Promised for you and for me;

See on the portals He's waiting and watching, Watching for you and for me.
Why should we linger and heed not His mercies, Mercies for you and for me?
Shadows are gathering, death beds are com-ing, Com-ing for you and for me.
Tho' we have sinn'd, He has mercy and pardon, Pardon for you and for me.

CHORUS.

Come home, come home, Ye who are wea-ry, come home,
Come home, come home,

Ear-nest-ly, ten-der-ly, Je-sus is call-ing, Call-ing, O sin-ner, come home!

No. 157.

Let Him In.

Rev. J. B. Atchinson.

E. O. Excell.

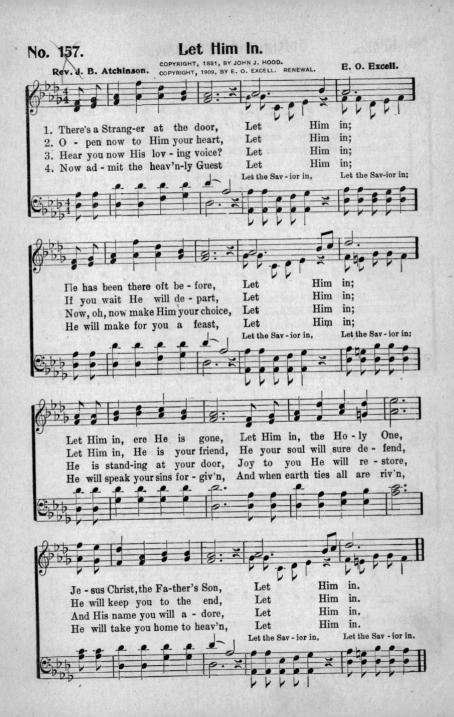

1. There's a Strang-er at the door, Let Him in;
2. O - pen now to Him your heart, Let Him in;
3. Hear you now His lov - ing voice? Let Him in;
4. Now ad - mit the heav'n-ly Guest Let Him in;

Let the Sav-ior in, Let the Sav-ior in;

He has been there oft be - fore, Let Him in;
If you wait He will de - part, Let Him in;
Now, oh, now make Him your choice, Let Him in;
He will make for you a feast, Let Him in;

Let the Sav-ior in, Let the Sav-ior in;

Let Him in, ere He is gone, Let Him in, the Ho - ly One,
Let Him in, He is your friend, He your soul will sure de - fend,
He is stand-ing at your door, Joy to you He will re - store,
He will speak your sins for - giv'n, And when earth ties all are riv'n,

Je - sus Christ, the Fa-ther's Son, Let Him in.
He will keep you to the end, Let Him in.
And His name you will a - dore, Let Him in.
He will take you home to heav'n, Let Him in.

Let the Sav - ior in, Let the Sav - ior in.

No. 158. Calling the Prodigal.

C. H. G.

COPYRIGHT, 1889, BY E. O. EXCELL.
WORDS AND MUSIC.

Chas. H. Gabriel.

1. God is call-ing the prod-i-gal, come with-out de-lay, Hear, O
2. Pa-tient, lov-ing, and ten-der-ly still the Fa-ther pleads, Hear, O
3. Come, there's bread in the house of thy Fa-ther, and to spare, Hear, O

hear Him call-ing, call-ing now for thee; Tho' you've wandered so
hear Him call-ing, call-ing now for thee; Oh! re-turn while the
hear Him call-ing, call-ing now for thee; Lo! the ta-ble is
for thee;

far from His presence, come today, Hear His loving voice calling still.....
Spir-it in mer-cy in-ter-cedes, Hear His loving voice calling still.....
spread and the feast is waiting there, Hear His loving voice calling still.....
calling still.

CHORUS.

Call - - ing now for thee, ... O wea - - - - ry prod-i-gal
Calling now for thee, Calling now for thee, Wea-ry prod-i-gal, come,

come; ...... Call - - ing now for thee, ...
wea-ry prod-i-gal, come; Call-ing now for thee, Call-ing now for thee,

Calling the Prodigal.

O wear - - - - - - y pro-di-gal, come! . . . .
Wear - y prod-i-gal, come,   wear - y prod-i-gal, come!

No. 159.

Wonderful Savior.

COPYRIGHT, 1909, BY E. O. EXCELL.

J. W. MacGill.   Arr. by E. O. E.

1. Je - sus has loved me— won - der - ful Sav - ior! Je - sus has
2. Je - sus has saved me— won - der - ful Sav - ior! Je - sus has
3. Je - sus will lead me— won - der - ful Sav - ior! Je - sus will
4. Je - sus will crown me— won - der - ful Sav - ior! Je - sus will

loved me, I can - not tell why; . . . . He came to res - cue
saved me, I can - not tell how; . . . . But this I do know,
lead me, I can - not tell where; . . . So I will fol - low
crown me, I can - not tell when; . . . White throne of splen-dor

sin - ners un - wor - thy, My heart He conquered, for Him I would die.
He came, my ran - som, Dy - ing on Calv'ry, with thorns on His brow.
thro' joy or sor - row, Sun-shine or tempest, since He leads me there.
hail I with gladness, Crowned in the pres-ence of an - gels and men.

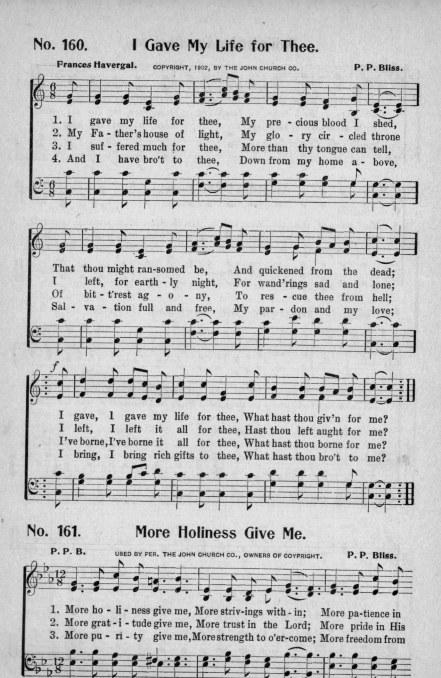

No. 160.   I Gave My Life for Thee.

Frances Havergal.   COPYRIGHT, 1902, BY THE JOHN CHURCH CO.   P. P. Bliss.

1. I gave my life for thee, My pre - cious blood I shed,
2. My Fa - ther's house of light, My glo - ry cir - cled throne
3. I suf - fered much for thee, More than thy tongue can tell,
4. And I have bro't to thee, Down from my home a - bove,

That thou might ran-somed be, And quickened from the dead;
I left, for earth - ly night, For wand'rings sad and lone;
Of bit - t'rest ag - o - ny, To res - cue thee from hell;
Sal - va - tion full and free, My par - don and my love;

I gave, I gave my life for thee, What hast thou giv'n for me?
I left, I left it all for thee, Hast thou left aught for me?
I've borne, I've borne it all for thee, What hast thou borne for me?
I bring, I bring rich gifts to thee, What hast thou bro't to me?

No. 161.   More Holiness Give Me.

P. P. B.   USED BY PER. THE JOHN CHURCH CO., OWNERS OF COYPRIGHT.   P. P. Bliss.

1. More ho - li - ness give me, More striv-ings with - in; More pa-tience in
2. More grat - i - tude give me, More trust in the Lord; More pride in His
3. More pu - ri - ty give me, More strength to o'er-come; More freedom from

More Holiness Give Me.

suf - f'ring, More sor - row for sin; More faith in my Sav - ior,
glo - ry, More hope in His Word; More tears for His sor - rows,
earth-stains, More long-ings for home; More fit for the king-dom,

rit.

More sense of His care; More joy in His serv-ice, More pur-pose in pray'r.
More pain at His grief: More meekness in tri - al, More praise for re-lief.
More used would I be; More bless-ed and ho - ly, More, Sav-ior, like Thee.

No. 162. Take My Life, and Let it Be.

F. R. Havergal.   Wm. B. Bradbury.

1. Take my life, and let it be Con - se - crat - ed, Lord, to Thee;
2. Take my feet, and let them be Swift and beau - ti - ful for Thee;
3. Take my sil - ver and my gold, Not a mite would I with-hold;
4. Take my will, and make it Thine, It shall be no lon - ger mine;

CHO.—Lord, I give my life to Thee, Thine for - ev - er - more to be;

D. C. for Chorus.

Take my hands, and let them move At the im - pulse of Thy love.
Take my voice, and let me sing Al - ways, on - ly, for my King.
Take my mo - ments and my days, Let them flow in cease-less praise.
Take my heart, it is Thine own, It shall be Thy roy - al throne.

Lord, I give my life to Thee, Thine for - ev - er-more to be.

No. 163.   I Love to Tell the Story.

Katharine Hankey. Refrain added.

William G. Fischer.

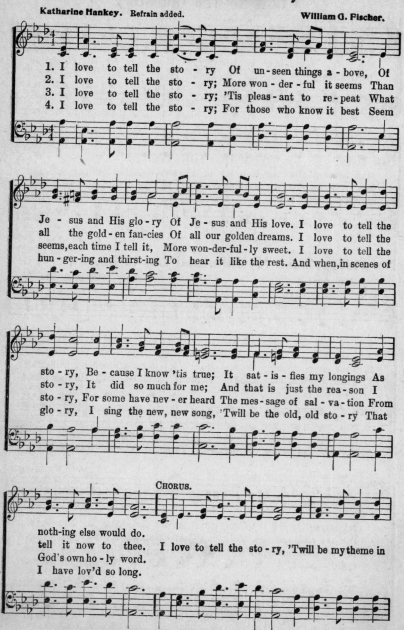

1. I love to tell the sto - ry Of un - seen things a - bove, Of
2. I love to tell the sto - ry; More won - der - ful it seems Than
3. I love to tell the sto - ry; 'Tis pleas - ant to re - peat What
4. I love to tell the sto - ry; For those who know it best Seem

Je - sus and His glo - ry Of Je - sus and His love. I love to tell the
all the gold - en fan - cies Of all our golden dreams. I love to tell the
seems, each time I tell it, More won - der - ful - ly sweet. I love to tell the
hun - ger - ing and thirst - ing To hear it like the rest. And when, in scenes of

sto - ry, Be - cause I know 'tis true; It sat - is - fies my longings As
sto - ry, It did so much for me; And that is just the rea - son I
sto - ry, For some have nev - er heard The mes - sage of sal - va - tion From
glo - ry, I sing the new, new song, 'Twill be the old, old sto - ry That

CHORUS.

noth - ing else would do.
tell it now to thee.   I love to tell the sto - ry, 'Twill be my theme in
God's own ho - ly word.
I have lov'd so long.

I Love to Tell the Story.

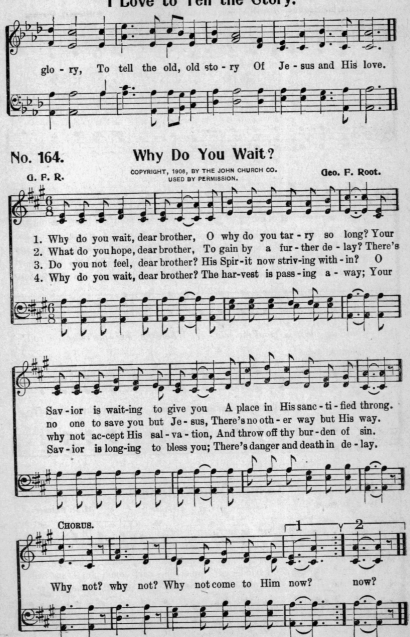

glo - ry, To tell the old, old sto - ry Of Je - sus and His love.

No. 164. Why Do You Wait?

G. F. R.

Geo. F. Root.

1. Why do you wait, dear brother, O why do you tar - ry so long? Your
2. What do you hope, dear brother, To gain by a fur - ther de - lay? There's
3. Do you not feel, dear brother? His Spir - it now striv - ing with - in? O
4. Why do you wait, dear brother? The har - vest is pass - ing a - way; Your

Sav - ior is wait - ing to give you A place in His sanc - ti - fied throng.
no one to save you but Je - sus, There's no oth - er way but His way.
why not ac - cept His sal - va - tion, And throw off thy bur - den of sin.
Sav - ior is long - ing to bless you; There's danger and death in de - lay.

CHORUS.

Why not? why not? Why not come to Him now? now?

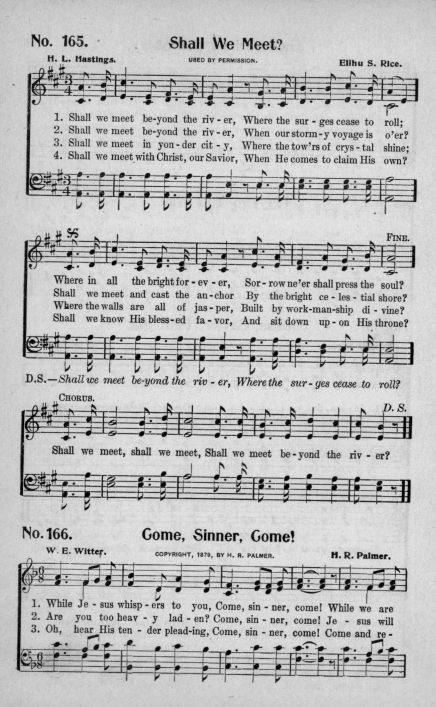

Come, Sinner Come!

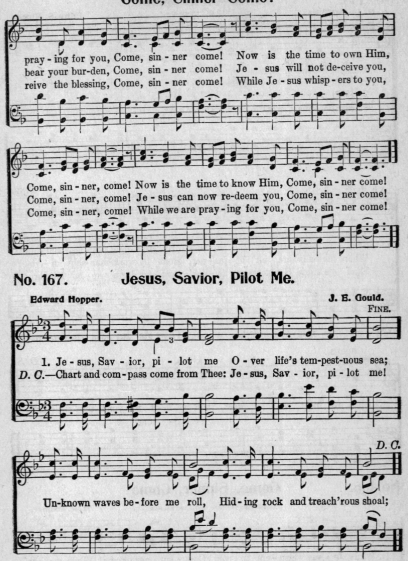

pray - ing for you, Come, sin - ner come! Now is the time to own Him,
bear your bur-den, Come, sin - ner come! Je - sus will not de-ceive you,
reive the blessing, Come, sin - ner come! While Je - sus whisp-ers to you,

Come, sin - ner, come! Now is the time to know Him, Come, sin - ner come!
Come, sin - ner, come! Je - sus can now re-deem you, Come, sin - ner come!
Come, sin - ner, come! While we are pray-ing for you, Come, sin - ner come!

No. 167. Jesus, Savior, Pilot Me.

Edward Hopper.   J. E. Gould.
FINE.

1. Je - sus, Sav - ior, pi - lot me O - ver life's tem-pest-uous sea;
D. C.—Chart and com-pass come from Thee: Je - sus, Sav - ior, pi - lot me!

D. C.

Un-known waves be-fore me roll, Hid-ing rock and treach'rous shoal;

2 As a mother stills her child,
    Thou canst hush the ocean wild;
    Boisterous waves obey Thy will
    When Thou say'st to them, "Be still!"
    Wondrous Sovereign of the sea,
    Jesus, Savior, pilot me!

3 When at last I near the shore,
    And the fearful breakers roar
    'Twixt me and the peaceful rest,
    Then, while leaning on Thy breast,
    May I hear Thee say to me,
    "Fear not, I will pilot thee!"

No. 168.   More About Jesus.

E. E. Hewitt.   Jno. R. Sweney.

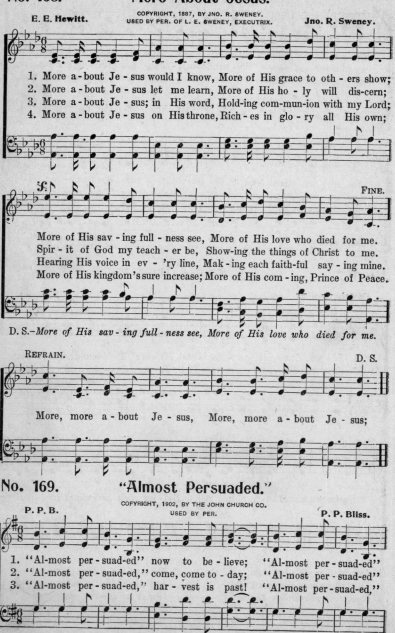

1. More a-bout Je-sus would I know, More of His grace to oth-ers show;
2. More a-bout Je-sus let me learn, More of His ho-ly will dis-cern;
3. More a-bout Je-sus; in His word, Hold-ing com-mun-ion with my Lord;
4. More a-bout Je-sus on His throne, Rich-es in glo-ry all His own;

More of His sav-ing full-ness see, More of His love who died for me.
Spir-it of God my teach-er be, Show-ing the things of Christ to me.
Hearing His voice in ev-'ry line, Mak-ing each faith-ful say-ing mine.
More of His kingdom's sure increase; More of His com-ing, Prince of Peace.

FINE.

D. S.—More of His sav-ing full-ness see, More of His love who died for me.

REFRAIN.   D. S.

More, more a-bout Je-sus, More, more a-bout Je-sus;

No. 169.   "Almost Persuaded."

P. P. B.   P. P. Bliss.

1. "Al-most per-suad-ed" now to be-lieve; "Al-most per-suad-ed"
2. "Al-most per-suad-ed," come, come to-day; "Al-most per-suad-ed"
3. "Al-most per-suad-ed," har-vest is past! "Al-most per-suad-ed,"

"Almost Persuaded."

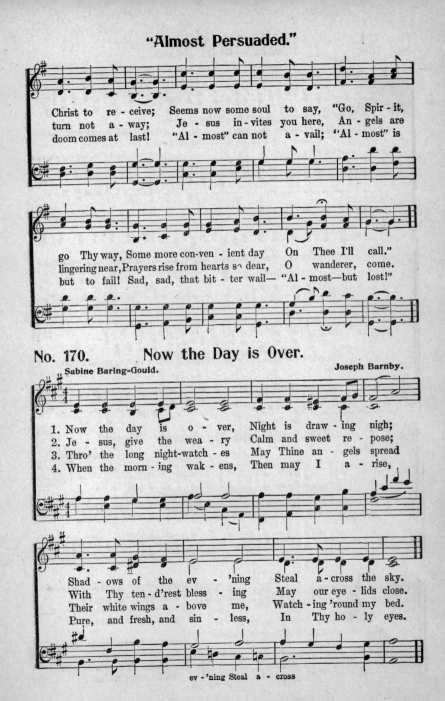

Christ to re - ceive; Seems now some soul to say, "Go, Spir - it,
turn not a - way; Je - sus in - vites you here, An - gels are
doom comes at last! "Al - most" can not a - vail; "Al - most" is

go Thy way, Some more con-ven - ient day On Thee I'll call."
lingering near, Prayers rise from hearts so dear, O wanderer, come.
but to fail! Sad, sad, that bit - ter wail— "Al - most—but lost!"

No. 170. Now the Day is Over.

Sabine Baring-Gould.

Joseph Barnby.

1. Now the day is o - ver, Night is draw - ing nigh;
2. Je - sus, give the wea - ry Calm and sweet re - pose;
3. Thro' the long night-watch - es May Thine an - gels spread
4. When the morn - ing wak - ens, Then may I a - rise,

Shad - ows of the ev - 'ning Steal a - cross the sky.
With Thy ten - d'rest bless - ing May our eye - lids close.
Their white wings a - bove me, Watch - ing 'round my bed.
Pure, and fresh, and sin - less, In Thy ho - ly eyes.

ev - 'ning Steal a - cross

No. 171.

At The Cross.

Isaac Watts.

R. E. Hudson.

1. { Alas! and did my Savior bleed, And did my Sov'reign die,
     Would He devote that sa- cred head For such a worm as I?

2. { Was it for crimes that I have done, He groan'd upon the tree,
     A - maz-ing pit-y, grace unknown! And love beyond degree

Chorus.

At the cross, at the cross, where I first saw the light, And the burden of my heart roll'd a-way, It was there by faith I received my sight, And now I am happy all the day.

roll'd a-way,

No. 172.

Alas! and Did My Savior Bleed?

Isaac Watts.

Hugh Wilson.

1. A - las! and did my Savior bleed? And did my Sov'reign die? Would He devote that sa-cred head For such a worm as I?

2. Was it for crimes that I have done, He groan'd upon the tree? A-maz-ing pit-y! grace unknown! And love be-yond de-gree!

3 Well might the sun in darkness hide,
And shut his glories in,
When Christ, the mighty Maker, died,
For man, the creature's sin.

4 But drops of grief can ne'er repay
The debt of love I owe:
Here, Lord, I give myself away,—
'Tis all that I can do.

No. 173. From Greenland's Icy Mountains.

Reginald Heber.   Lowell Mason.

1. From Greenland's i - cy moun-tains, From In-dia's cor - al strand, Where Af-ric's
2. Shall we, whose souls are light - ed With wis-dom from on high, Shall we to
3. Waft, waft, ye winds, His sto - ry, And you, ye wa-ters, roll, Till, like a

sun - ny foun-tains Roll down their golden sand; From man - y an ancient riv - er, From
men be-night - ed The lamp of life de - ny? Sal - va - tion! O sal - va - tion! The
sea of glo - ry, It spreads from pole to pole: Till o'er our ransomed na-ture The

many a palm-y plain, They call us to de - liv - er Their land from error's chain.
joy - ful sound proclaim, Till earth's remotest na - tion Has learned Messiah's name.
Lamb for sinners slain, Re-deem-er, King, Cre-a - tor, In bliss re-turns to reign.

No. 174. Ye Christian Heralds!

C. Zeunder.

1. Ye Chris-tian her - alds! go pro-claim Sal - va-tion thro' Im - man - uel's name;
2. He'll shield you with a wall of fire, With flam-ing zeal your hearts in - spire,
3. And when our la - bors all are o'er, Then shall we meet to part no more—

To dis - tant climes the ti - dings bear, And plant the Rose of Shar - on there.
Bid rag - ing winds their fu - ry cease, And hush the tem - pest in - to peace.
Meet with the blood-bought throng to fall, And crown our Je - sus—Lord of all.

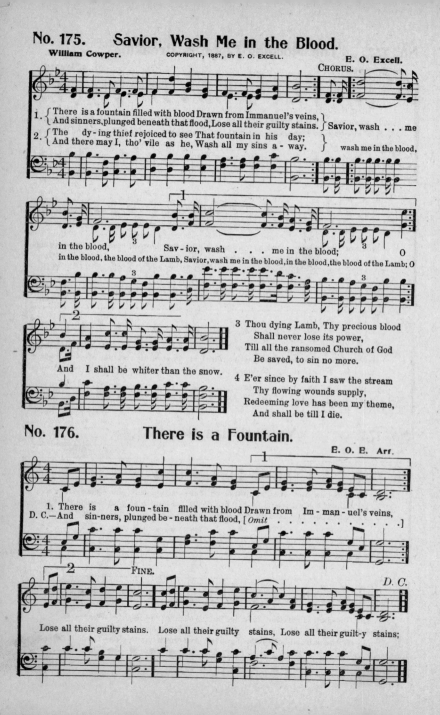

No. 175. Savior, Wash Me in the Blood.

William Cowper.   COPYRIGHT, 1887, BY E. O. EXCELL.   E. O. Excell.

CHORUS.

1. { There is a fountain filled with blood Drawn from Immanuel's veins,
   { And sinners, plunged beneath that flood, Lose all their guilty stains. } Savior, wash . . . me

2. { The dy-ing thief rejoiced to see That fountain in his day;
   { And there may I, tho' vile as he, Wash all my sins a-way. } wash me in the blood,

in the blood, Sav-ior, wash . . . me in the blood;

in the blood, the blood of the Lamb, Savior, wash me in the blood, in the blood, the blood of the Lamb; O

And   I shall be whiter than the snow.

3 Thou dying Lamb, Thy precious blood
   Shall never lose its power,
Till all the ransomed Church of God
   Be saved, to sin no more.

4 E'er since by faith I saw the stream
   Thy flowing wounds supply,
Redeeming love has been my theme,
   And shall be till I die.

No. 176. There is a Fountain.

E. O. E. Arr.

1. There is   a foun-tain filled with blood Drawn from Im-man-uel's veins,
D. C.—And   sin-ners, plunged be-neath that flood, [Omit . . . .]

FINE.

D. C.

Lose all their guilty stains.   Lose all their guilty   stains, Lose all their guilt-y stains;

No. 177. The Morning Light is Breaking.

S. F. Smith. G. J. Webb.

1. The morn-ing light is break-ing, The darkness dis-ap-pears; The sons of earth are wak-ing To pen-i-ten-tial tears; Each breeze that sweeps the o-cean Brings ti-dings from a-far, Of na-tions in com-mo-tion, Prepared for Zi-on's war.

2. See hea-then na-tions bend-ing Be-fore the God of love, And thousand hearts as-cend-ing In grat-i-tude a-bove; While sinners, now con-fess-ing, The gos-pel's call o-bey, And seek a Sav-ior's bless-ing, A na-tion in a day.

3. Blest riv-er of sal-va-tion, Pur-sue thine onward way; Flow thou to ev-'ry na-tion, Nor in thy rich-ness stay; Stay not till all the low-ly Tri-umphant reach their home; Stay not till all the ho-ly Proclaim, "The Lord is come!"

No. 178. Stand Up for Jesus.

1 Stand up, stand up for Jesus,
  Ye soldiers of the cross;
Lift high His royal banner,
  It must not suffer loss:
From victory unto victory
  His army shall He lead,
Till every foe is vanquished
  And Christ is Lord indeed.

2 Stand up, stand up for Jesus,
  The trumpet call obey;
Forth to the mighty conflict,
  In this His glorious day:
"Ye that are men, now serve Him,"
  Against unnumbered foes;
Your courage rise with danger,
  And strength to strength oppose.

3 Stand up, stand up for Jesus,
  Stand in His strength alone;
The arm of flesh will fail you;
  Ye dare not trust your own:
Put on the gospel armor,
  Each piece put on with prayer;
Where duty calls, or danger,
  Be never wanting there.

4 Stand up, stand up for Jesus,
  The strife will not be long;
This day the noise of battle,
  The next the victor's song:
To him that overcometh,
  A crown of life shall be;
He with the King of glory
  Shall reign eternally.

—*George Duffield.*

Onward, Christian Soldiers.

Sabine Baring-Gould.   Arthur Sullivan.

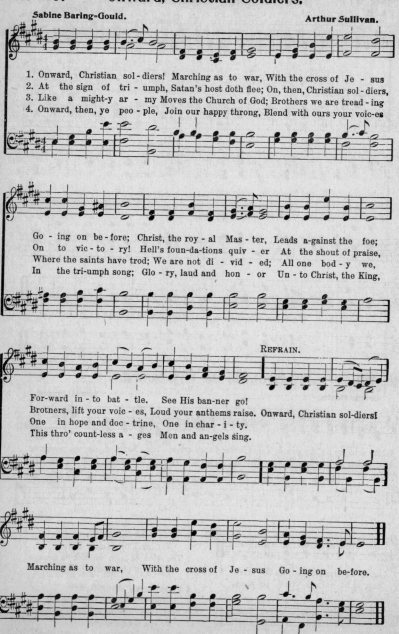

1. Onward, Christian sol - diers! Marching as to war, With the cross of Je - sus
2. At the sign of tri - umph, Satan's host doth flee; On, then, Christian sol - diers,
3. Like a might-y ar - my Moves the Church of God; Brothers we are tread - ing
4. Onward, then, ye peo - ple, Join our happy throng, Blend with ours your voic - es

Go - ing on be - fore; Christ, the roy - al Mas - ter, Leads a-gainst the foe;
On to vic - to - ry! Hell's foun-da-tions quiv - er At the shout of praise,
Where the saints have trod; We are not di - vid - ed; All one bod - y we,
In the tri - umph song; Glo - ry, laud and hon - or Un - to Christ, the King,

Refrain.

For-ward in - to bat - tle. See His ban-ner go!
Brotners, lift your voic - es, Loud your anthems raise. Onward, Christian sol-diers!
One in hope and doc - trine, One in char - i - ty.
This thro' count-less a - ges Men and an-gels sing.

Marching as to war, With the cross of Je - sus Go - ing on be-fore.

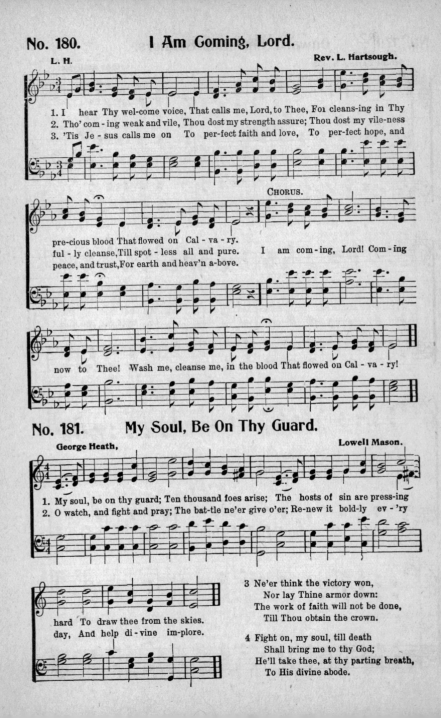

No. 180.   I Am Coming, Lord.

L. H.   Rev. L. Hartsough.

1. I hear Thy wel-come voice, That calls me, Lord, to Thee, For cleans-ing in Thy
2. Tho' com-ing weak and vile, Thou dost my strength assure; Thou dost my vile-ness
3. 'Tis Je-sus calls me on To per-fect faith and love, To per-fect hope, and

CHORUS.

pre-cious blood That flowed on Cal-va-ry.
ful-ly cleanse, Till spot-less all and pure.
peace, and trust, For earth and heav'n a-bove.

I am com-ing, Lord! Com-ing

now to Thee! Wash me, cleanse me, in the blood That flowed on Cal-va-ry!

No. 181.   My Soul, Be On Thy Guard.

George Heath,   Lowell Mason.

1. My soul, be on thy guard; Ten thousand foes arise; The hosts of sin are press-ing
2. O watch, and fight and pray; The bat-tle ne'er give o'er; Re-new it bold-ly ev-'ry

hard To draw thee from the skies.
day, And help di-vine im-plore.

3 Ne'er think the victory won,
    Nor lay Thine armor down:
The work of faith will not be done,
    Till Thou obtain the crown.

4 Fight on, my soul, till death
    Shall bring me to thy God;
He'll take thee, at thy parting breath,
    To His divine abode.

What a Friend.

H. Bonar.

C. C. Converse.

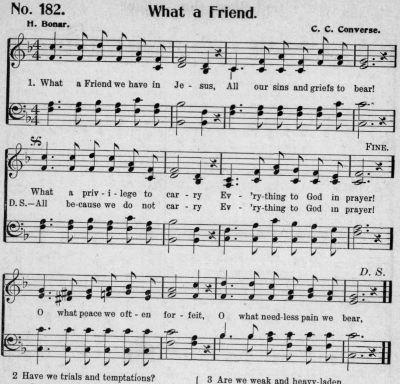

1. What a Friend we have in Je - sus, All our sins and griefs to bear!

What a priv - i - lege to car - ry Ev - 'ry-thing to God in prayer!
D. S.—All be-cause we do not car - ry Ev - 'ry-thing to God in prayer!

O what peace we oft - en for - feit, O what need-less pain we bear,

2 Have we trials and temptations?
    Is there trouble anywhere?
We should never be discouraged,
    Take it to the Lord in prayer.
Can we find a friend so faithful,
    Who will all our sorrows share?
Jesus knows our every weakness,
    Take it to the Lord in prayer.

3 Are we weak and heavy-laden,
    Cumbered with a load of care?—
Precious Savior, still our refuge,—
    Take it to the Lord in prayer.
Do thy friends despise, forsake thee?
    Take it to the Lord in prayer;
In His arms He'll take and shield thee,
    Thou wilt find a solace there.

No. 183.   God Bless Our School!

W. W. Hamilton.

Tune—"America."

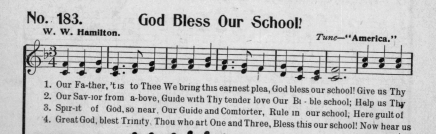

1. Our Fa-ther, 'tis to Thee We bring this earnest plea, God bless our school! Give us Thy
2. Our Sav-ior from a-bove, Guide with Thy tender love Our Bi - ble school; Help us Thy
3. Spir-it of God, so near, Our Guide and Comforter, Rule in our school; Here guilt of
4. Great God, blest Trinity, Thou who art One and Three, Bless this our school! Now hear us

God Bless Our School!

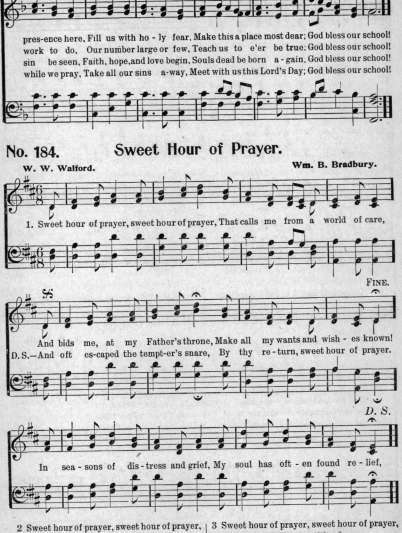

pres-ence here, Fill us with ho - ly fear, Make this a place most dear; God bless our school!
work to do, Our number large or few, Teach us to e'er be true; God bless our school!
sin be seen, Faith, hope, and love begin, Souls dead be born a - gain; God bless our school!
while we pray, Take all our sins a-way, Meet with us this Lord's Day; God bless our school!

No. 184. Sweet Hour of Prayer.

W. W. Walford.   Wm. B. Bradbury.

1. Sweet hour of prayer, sweet hour of prayer, That calls me from a world of care,

FINE.

And bids me, at my Father's throne, Make all my wants and wish - es known!
D. S.—And oft es-caped the tempt-er's snare, By thy re - turn, sweet hour of prayer.

D. S.

In sea - sons of dis - tress and grief, My soul has oft - en found re - lief,

2 Sweet hour of prayer, sweet hour of prayer,
The joys I feel, the bliss I share,
Of those whose anxious spirits burn
With strong desires for thy return!
With such I hasten to the place
Where God, my Savior, shows His face,
And gladly take my station there,
And wait for thee, sweet hour of prayer.

3 Sweet hour of prayer, sweet hour of prayer,
Thy wings shall my petition bear
To Him, whose truth and faithfulness
Engage the waiting soul to bless:
And since He bids me seek His face,
Believe His word, and trust His grace,
I'll cast on Him my every care,
And wait for thee, sweet hour of prayer.

No. 185. Just as I Am.

Charlotte Elliott,　　　　　　　　　　　　　　　　　　　Wm. Bradbury.

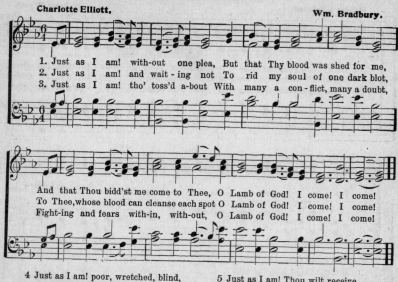

1. Just as I am! with-out one plea, But that Thy blood was shed for me,
2. Just as I am! and wait-ing not To rid my soul of one dark blot,
3. Just as I am! tho' toss'd a-bout With many a con-flict, many a doubt,

And that Thou bidd'st me come to Thee, O Lamb of God! I come! I come!
To Thee, whose blood can cleanse each spot O Lamb of God! I come! I come!
Fight-ing and fears with-in, with-out, O Lamb of God! I come! I come!

4 Just as I am! poor, wretched, blind,
　Sight, riches, healing of the mind,
　Yea, all I need in Thee to find,
　O Lamb of God! I come! I come!

5 Just as I am! Thou wilt receive,
　Wilt welcome, pardon, cleanse, relieve:
　Because Thy promise I believe,
　O Lamb of God! I come! I come!

No. 186. Holy Spirit, Faithful Guide.

M. M. W.　　　　　　　　　　　　　　　　　　　　　　　M. M. Wells.

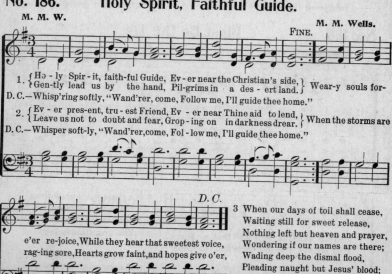

FINE.

1. { Ho-ly Spir-it, faith-ful Guide, Ev-er near the Christian's side, }
   { Gen-tly lead us by the hand, Pil-grims in a des-ert land. } Wear-y souls for-
D. C.—Whisp'ring softly, "Wand'rer, come, Follow me, I'll guide thee home."

2. { Ev-er pres-ent, tru-est Friend, Ev-er near Thine aid to lend, }
   { Leave us not to doubt and fear, Grop-ing on in darkness drear. } When the storms are
D. C.—Whisper soft-ly, "Wand'rer, come, Fol-low me, I'll guide thee home."

D. C.

e'er re-joice, While they hear that sweetest voice,
rag-ing sore, Hearts grow faint, and hopes give o'er,

3 When our days of toil shall cease,
　Waiting still for sweet release,
　Nothing left but heaven and prayer,
　Wondering if our names are there;
　Wading deep the dismal flood,
　Pleading naught but Jesus' blood;
　Whisper softly, "Wanderer, come,
　Follow me, I'll guide thee home."

No. 187.   Come, Thou Fount.

Robert Robinson.

John Wyeth.

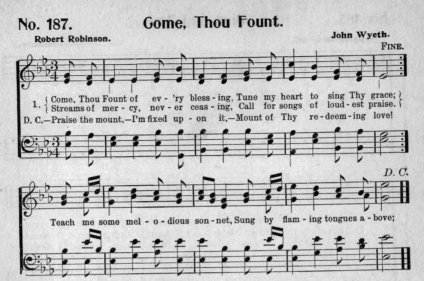

1. { Come, Thou Fount of ev - 'ry bless - ing, Tune my heart to sing Thy grace;
   { Streams of mer - cy, nev - er ceas - ing, Call for songs of loud - est praise.

D. C.—Praise the mount,—I'm fixed up - on it,—Mount of Thy re - deem - ing love!

Teach me some mel - o - dious son - net, Sung by flam - ing tongues a - bove;

2 Here I'll raise my Ebenezer,
   Hither by Thy help I'm come;
And I hope, by Thy good pleasure,
   Safely to arrive at home.
Jesus sought me when a stranger,
   Wandering from the fold of God;
He, to rescue me from danger,
   Interposed His precious blood.

3 Oh, to grace how great a debtor
   Daily I'm constrained to be!
Let Thy goodness, like a fetter,
   Bind my wandering heart to Thee.
Prone to wander, Lord, I feel it,
   Prone to leave the God I love;
Here's my heart, oh, take and seal it,
   Seal it for Thy courts above.

No. 188.   Blest Be the Tie.

John Fawcett.

Hans George Naegeli.

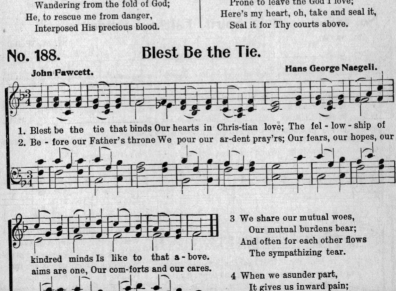

1. Blest be the tie that binds Our hearts in Chris-tian love; The fel - low - ship of
2. Be - fore our Father's throne We pour our ar-dent pray'rs; Our fears, our hopes, our

kindred minds Is like to that a - bove.
aims are one, Our com-forts and our cares.

3 We share our mutual woes,
   Our mutual burdens bear;
And often for each other flows
   The sympathizing tear.

4 When we asunder part,
   It gives us inward pain;
But we shall still be joined in heart,
   And hope to meet again.

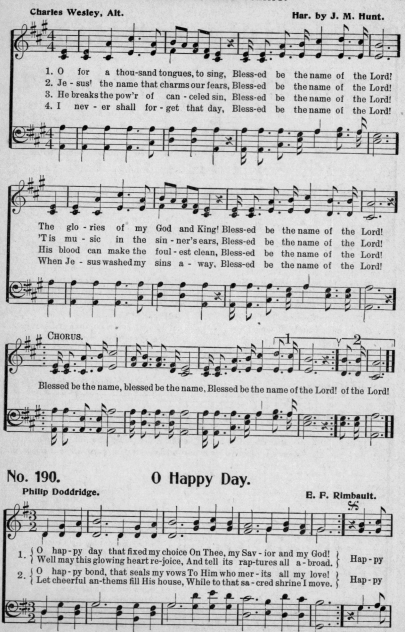

No. 189. **Blessed Be the Name.**

Charles Wesley, Alt.   Har. by J. M. Hunt.

1. O for a thou-sand tongues, to sing, Bless-ed be the name of the Lord!
2. Je - sus! the name that charms our fears, Bless-ed be the name of the Lord!
3. He breaks the pow'r of can - celed sin, Bless-ed be the name of the Lord!
4. I nev - er shall for - get that day, Bless-ed be the name of the Lord!

The glo - ries of my God and King! Bless-ed be the name of the Lord!
'Tis mu - sic in the sin - ner's ears, Bless-ed be the name of the Lord!
His blood can make the foul - est clean, Bless-ed be the name of the Lord!
When Je - sus washed my sins a - way, Bless-ed be the name of the Lord!

CHORUS.

Blessed be the name, blessed be the name, Blessed be the name of the Lord! of the Lord!

No. 190. **O Happy Day.**

Philip Doddridge.   E. F. Rimbault.

1. { O hap-py day that fixed my choice On Thee, my Sav - ior and my God! } Hap - py
   { Well may this glowing heart re-joice, And tell its rap-tures all a - broad. }

2. { O hap-py bond, that seals my vows To Him who mer - its all my love! } Hap - py
   { Let cheerful an-thems fill His house, While to that sa - cred shrine I move. }

O Happy Day.

FINE.

day, hap-py day, When Je-sus washed my sins a-way. He taught me how to watch and

D. S.

pray, And live re-joi-cing ev-'ry day;

3 'T is done, the great transaction's done;
  I am my Lord's, and He is mine;
  He drew me, and I followed on,
  Charmed to confess the voice divine.

4 Now rest, my long-divided heart,
  Fixed on this blissful center, rest;
  Nor ever from thy Lord depart,
  With Him of every good possessed.

No. 191. Sweet By-and-By.

S. Fillmore Bennett.   BY PERMISSION.   Jos. P. Webster.

1. { There's a land that is fair-er than day, And by faith we can see it a - far;
     For the Fa-ther waits o - ver the way, To pre- [*Omit...........................*] }

CHORUS.

pare us a dwelling-place there. In the sweet   by-and - by,   We shall meet on that
In the sweet   by-and-by,

beau-ti-ful shore;   by-and - by,   We shall meet on that beautiful shore.
        by-and-by;   by-and-by,

2 We shall sing on that beautiful shore
  The melodious songs of the blest,
  And our spirits shall sorrow no more,
  Not a sigh for the blessing of rest.

3 To our bountiful Father above,
  We will offer our tribute of praise,
  For the glorious gift of His love,
  And the blessings that hallow our days.

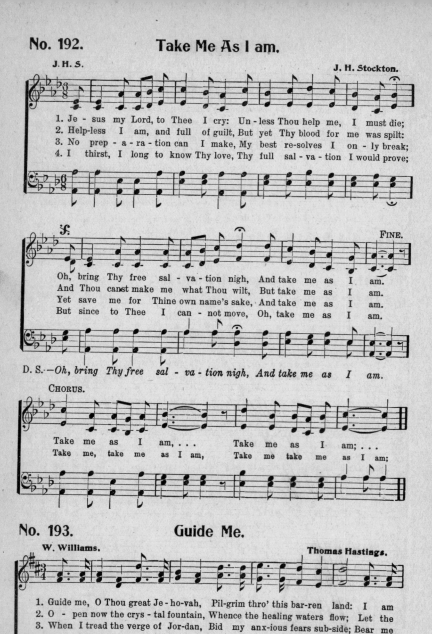

No. 192.
Take Me As I am.

J. H. S.

J. H. Stockton.

1. Je - sus my Lord, to Thee I cry: Un - less Thou help me, I must die;
2. Help-less I am, and full of guilt, But yet Thy blood for me was spilt:
3. No prep - a - ra - tion can I make, My best re-solves I on - ly break;
4. I thirst, I long to know Thy love, Thy full sal - va - tion I would prove;

Oh, bring Thy free sal - va - tion nigh, And take me as I am.
And Thou canst make me what Thou wilt, But take me as I am.
Yet save me for Thine own name's sake, And take me as I am.
But since to Thee I can - not move, Oh, take me as I am.

FINE.

D. S.—*Oh, bring Thy free sal - va - tion nigh, And take me as I am.*

CHORUS.

Take me as I am, . . . Take me as I am; . . .
Take me, take me as I am, Take me take me as I am;

No. 193.
Guide Me.

W. Williams.

Thomas Hastings.

1. Guide me, O Thou great Je - ho-vah, Pil-grim thro' this bar-ren land: I am
2. O - pen now the crys - tal fountain, Whence the healing waters flow; Let the
3. When I tread the verge of Jor-dan, Bid my anx-ious fears sub-side; Bear me

Guide Me.

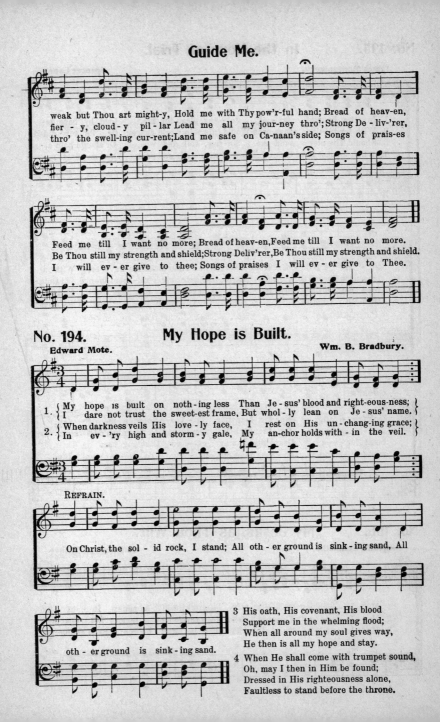

weak but Thou art might-y, Hold me with Thy pow'r-ful hand; Bread of heav-en,
fier - y, cloud - y pil - lar Lead me all my jour-ney thro'; Strong De - liv'rer,
thro' the swell-ing cur-rent; Land me safe on Ca-naan's side; Songs of prais-es

Feed me till I want no more; Bread of heav-en, Feed me till I want no more.
Be Thou still my strength and shield; Strong Deliv'rer, Be Thou still my strength and shield.
I will ev - er give to thee; Songs of praises I will ev - er give to Thee.

No. 194. My Hope is Built.

Edward Mote.

Wm. B. Bradbury.

1. { My hope is built on noth-ing less Than Je - sus' blood and right-eous-ness;
    { I dare not trust the sweet-est frame, But whol - ly lean on Je - sus' name.
2. { When darkness veils His love - ly face, I rest on His un - chang-ing grace;
    { In ev - 'ry high and storm - y gale, My an-chor holds with - in the veil.

REFRAIN.

On Christ, the sol - id rock, I stand; All oth - er ground is sink - ing sand, All

oth - er ground is sink - ing sand.

3 His oath, His covenant, His blood
Support me in the whelming flood;
When all around my soul gives way,
He then is all my hope and stay.

4 When He shall come with trumpet sound,
Oh, may I then in Him be found;
Dressed in His righteousness alone,
Faultless to stand before the throne.

No. 195. In the Hour of Trial.

James Montgomery.

Spencer Lane.

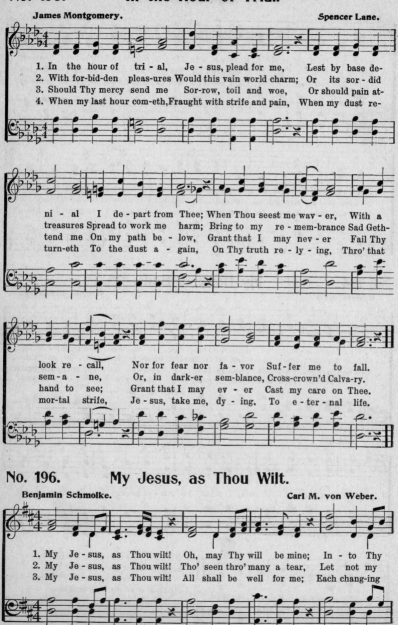

1. In the hour of tri - al, Je - sus, plead for me, Lest by base de-
2. With for-bid-den pleas-ures Would this vain world charm; Or its sor - did
3. Should Thy mercy send me Sor-row, toil and woe, Or should pain at-
4. When my last hour com-eth, Fraught with strife and pain, When my dust re-

ni - al I de-part from Thee; When Thou seest me wav - er, With a
treasures Spread to work me harm; Bring to my re - mem-brance Sad Geth-
tend me On my path be - low, Grant that I may nev - er Fail Thy
turn-eth To the dust a - gain, On Thy truth re - ly - ing, Thro' that

look re - call, Nor for fear nor fa - vor Suf-fer me to fall.
sem-a - ne, Or, in dark-er sem-blance, Cross-crown'd Calva-ry.
hand to see; Grant that I may ev - er Cast my care on Thee.
mor-tal strife, Je - sus, take me, dy - ing, To e - ter - nal life.

No. 196. My Jesus, as Thou Wilt.

Benjamin Schmolke.

Carl M. von Weber.

1. My Je - sus, as Thou wilt! Oh, may Thy will be mine; In - to Thy
2. My Je - sus, as Thou wilt! Tho' seen thro' many a tear, Let not my
3. My Je - sus, as Thou wilt! All shall be well for me; Each chang-ing

My Jesus, as Thou Wilt.

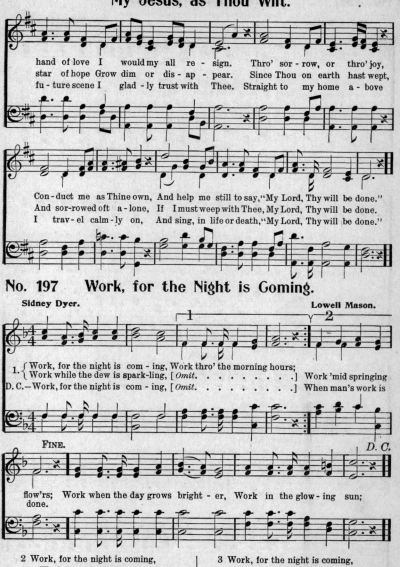

hand of love I would my all re - sign. Thro' sor - row, or thro' joy,
star of hope Grow dim or dis - ap - pear. Since Thou on earth hast wept,
fu - ture scene I glad - ly trust with Thee. Straight to my home a - bove

Con - duct me as Thine own, And help me still to say, "My Lord, Thy will be done."
And sor-rowed oft a - lone, If I must weep with Thee, My Lord, Thy will be done.
I trav - el calm - ly on, And sing, in life or death, "My Lord, Thy will be done."

No. 197   Work, for the Night is Coming.

Sidney Dyer.   Lowell Mason.

1. { Work, for the night is com - ing, Work thro' the morning hours;
   { Work while the dew is spark-ling, [Omit. . . . .] Work 'mid springing
D. C.—Work, for the night is com - ing, [Omit. . . . .] When man's work is

FINE.   D. C.

flow'rs; Work when the day grows bright - er, Work in the glow-ing sun;
done.

2 Work, for the night is coming,
    Work through the sunny noon;
Fill brightest hours with labor,
    Rest comes sure and soon.
Give every flying minute
    Something to keep in store;
Work, for the night is coming,
    When man works no more.

3 Work, for the night is coming,
    Under the sunset skies;
While their bright tints are glowing,
    Work, for daylight flies.
Work till the last beam fadeth,
    Fadeth to shine no more;
Work while the night is darkening,
    When man's work is o'er.

No. 198.   We're Marching to Zion.

Rev. I. Watts.   **Rev. Robert Lowry.**

1. Come, we that love the Lord, And let our joys be known, Join in a song with
2. Let those re - fuse to sing Who nev - er knew our God; But chil-dren of the
3. The hill of Zi - on yields] A thou-sand sa-cred sweets, Be-fore we reach the
4. Then let our songs a-bound, And ev - 'ry tear be dry; We're marching thro' Im-

sweet accord, Join in a song with sweet accord, And thus sur-round the throne,
heav'n-ly King, But chil-dren of the heav'n-ly King, May speak their joys a-broad,
heav'n-ly fields, Be - fore we reach the heav'nly fields, Or walk the gold - en streets,
manuel's ground, We're marching thro' Immanuel's ground, To fair-er worlds on high,

And thus surround the throne, And thus

Chorus.

And thus surround the throne.
May speak their joys a - broad.   We're marching to Zi - on, Beau-ti-ful, beau-ti-ful
Or walk the gold-en streets.
To fair - er worlds on high.
sur - round   the   throne.   We're marching on to Zi - on,

Zi - on; We're marching upward to Zi - on, The beau - ti - ful cit - y of God.
Zi-on, Zi-on,

No. 199. Savior, Breathe an Evening Blessing.

James Edmeston.

D. Bortnianski.

1. Sav-ior, breathe an eve-ning bless-ing, Ere re-pose our spir-its seal;
Sin and want we come con-fess-ing; Thou canst save and Thou canst heal.

2. Tho' the night be dark and drear-y, Dark-ness can-not hide from Thee;
Thou art He who, nev-er wea-ry, Watcheth where Thy peo-ple be.

Though de-struc-tion walk a-round us, Tho' the ar-row near us fly,
Should swift death this night o'er-take us, And our couch be-come our tomb,

An - gel guards from Thee sur-round us, We are safe if Thou art nigh.
May the morn in Heav'n a-wake us, Clad in light and death-less bloom.

No. 200. Must Jesus Bear the Cross?

Thos. Shepherd.

Tune,—Maitland. C. M.

1. Must Je-sus bear the cross alone, And all the world go free? No, there's a cross for

2. The con-se-crat-ed cross I'll bear, Till death shall set me free; And then go home my

ev-'ry one, And there's a cross for me.
crown to wear, For there's a crown for me.

3 Upon the crystal pavement, down
At Jesus' pierced feet,
With joy I'll cast my golden crown,
And His dear name repeat.

4 Oh, precious cross! oh, glorious crown,
Oh, resurrection day!
Ye angels from the stars come down
And bear my soul away.

No. 201.   Jesus Paid It All.

Mrs. E. M. Hall.   John T. Grape.

1. I hear the Sav-ior say, "Thy strength indeed is small; Child of weak-ness,
2. Lord, now in-deed I find Thy power, and Thine a-lone, Can change the
3. For noth-ing good have I Where-by Thy grace to claim— I'll wash my

CHORUS.

watch and pray, Find in me thine all in all."
lep - er's spots, And melt the heart of stone. Je - sus paid it all,
gar-ments white In the blood of Cal-v'ry's Lamb.

All to Him I owe; Sin had left a crimson stain, He washed it white as snow.

No. 202.   Jesus Calls Us.

Cecil F. Alexander.   W. H. Jude.

1. Je-sus calls us: o'er the tumult Of our life's wild restless sea, Day by day His sweet voice
2. Jesus calls us from the worship Of the vain world's golden shore; From each idol that would

soundeth, Saying, "Christian, follow Me."
keep us, Saying, "Christian, love Me more."

3 In our joys and in our sorrows,
   Days of toil and hours of ease;
Still He calls, in cares and pleasures,
   "That we love Him more than these."

4 Jesus calls us: by Thy mercies,
   Savior, make us hear Thy call,
Give our hearts to Thine obedience,
   Serve and love Thee best of all.

No. 203. Shall We Gather at the River?

R. L.

Robert Lowry.

1. Shall we gath-er at the riv - er, Where bright angel feet have trod; With its
2. On the mar-gin of the riv - er, Wash-ing up its sil-ver spray, We will
3. Ere we reach the shining riv - er, Lay we ev-'ry bur-den down; Grace our
4. Soon we'll reach the shining riv - er, Soon our pil-grim-age will cease; Soon our

CHORUS.

crys-tal tide for - ev - er Flow-ing by the throne of God?
walk and worship ev - er, All the hap-py, gold-en day.   { Yes,   we'll gath-er
spir-its will de - liv - er, And provide a robe and crown. { Gather with the saints
hap-py hearts will quiv-er With the mel - o - dy of peace.

1
at the riv - er, The beautiful, the beau-ti-ful riv - er,—

2
at the riv - er That [Omit . . . .] flows by the throne of God.

No. 204. Come to Jesus.

Unknown.

Arr. by E. O. E.

1. Come to Je - sus, come to Je - sus, Come to Je - sus just now; Just now come to
2. He will save you, He will save you, He will save you just now; Just now He will

Je - sus, Come to Je - sus just now.
save you, He will save you just now.

3 He is able.
4 He is willing.
5 Call upon Him.
6 He will hear you.
7 He'll forgive you.
8 He will cleanse you.
9 Jesus loves you.
10 Only trust Him.

No. 205. O Could I Speak.

S. Medley.

Dr. Lowell Mason.

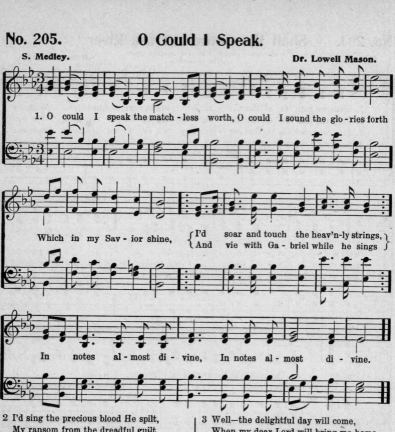

1. O could I speak the match-less worth, O could I sound the glo-ries forth

Which in my Sav-ior shine, { I'd soar and touch the heav'n-ly strings,
And vie with Ga-briel while he sings }

In notes al-most di-vine, In notes al-most di-vine.

2 I'd sing the precious blood He spilt,
My ransom from the dreadful guilt
Of sin, and wrath divine!
I'd sing His glorious righteousness,
In which all-perfect heavenly dress
My soul shall ever shine.

3 Well—the delightful day will come,
When my dear Lord will bring me home,
And I shall see His face:
Then with my Savior, Brother, Friend,
A blest eternity I'll spend,
Triumphant in His grace.

No. 206. My Happy Home.

Anon.

E. O. Excell.

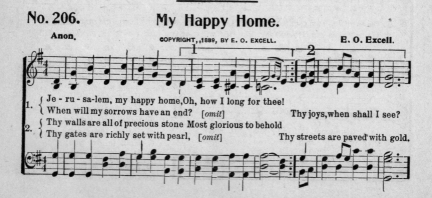

1. { Je - ru - sa-lem, my happy home, Oh, how I long for thee!
{ When will my sorrows have an end? [omit] Thy joys, when shall I see?

2. { Thy walls are all of precious stone Most glorious to behold
{ Thy gates are richly set with pearl, [omit] Thy streets are paved with gold.

My Happy Home.

CHORUS.

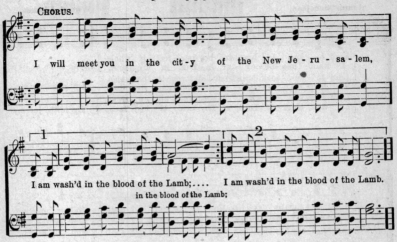

I will meet you in the cit-y of the New Je - ru - sa - lem,

I am wash'd in the blood of the Lamb;.... I am wash'd in the blood of the Lamb.

in the blood of the Lamb;

3 Thy gardens and thy pleasant streams
  My study long have been—
  Such sparkling gems by human sight
  Have never yet been seen.

4 Reach down, reach down thine arms of grace
  And cause me to ascend
  Where congregations ne'er break up
  And praises never end,

No. 207. My Faith Looks Up to Thee.

Ray Palmer.   Lowell Mason.

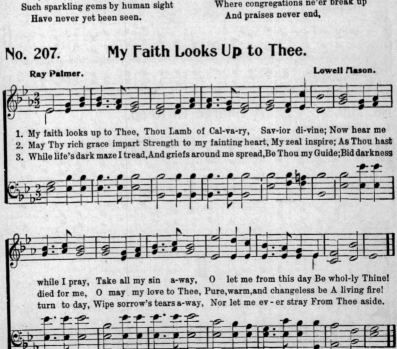

1. My faith looks up to Thee, Thou Lamb of Cal-va-ry, Sav-ior di-vine; Now hear me
2. May Thy rich grace impart Strength to my fainting heart, My zeal inspire; As Thou hast
3. While life's dark maze I tread, And griefs around me spread, Be Thou my Guide; Bid darkness

while I pray, Take all my sin a-way, O let me from this day Be whol-ly Thine!
died for me, O may my love to Thee, Pure, warm, and changeless be A living fire!
turn to day, Wipe sorrow's tears a-way, Nor let me ev - er stray From Thee aside.

No. 208.   Whiter Than Snow.

James Nicholson.   BY PERMISSION.   Wm. G. Fischer.

1. { Lord Je - sus, I long to be per - fect - ly whole;
   { I want Thee for - ev - er to live in my soul, } Break down ev - 'ry

2. { Lord Je - sus, look down from Thy throne in the skies,
   { And help me to make a com - plete sac - ri - fice; } I give up my-

3. { Lord Je - sus, for this I most hum - bly en - treat,
   { I wait, bless - ed Lord, at Thy cru - ci - fied feet, } By faith, for my

i - dol, cast out ev - 'ry foe; Now wash me and I shall be whit-er than snow.
self, and what-ev - er I know, Now wash me and I shall be whit-er than snow.
cleans-ing, I see Thy blood flow, Now wash me and I shall be whit-er than snow.

CHORUS.

Whiter than snow, yes, whiter than snow; Now wash me and I shall be whit-er than snow.

No. 209.   A Charge to Keep.

Charles Wesley.   Lowell Mason.

1. A charge to keep I have, A God to glo - ri - fy; A nev - er dy - ing
2. To serve the pres - ent age, My call - ing to ful - fill, Oh, may it all my

soul to save And fit it for the sky.
pow'rs engage, To do my Mas-ter's will.

3 Arm me with jealous care,
    And in Thy sight to live;
    And oh, Thy servant, Lord, prepare,
    A strict account to give.

4 Help me to watch and pray,
    And on Thyself rely,
    Assured, if I my trust betray,
    I shall forever die.

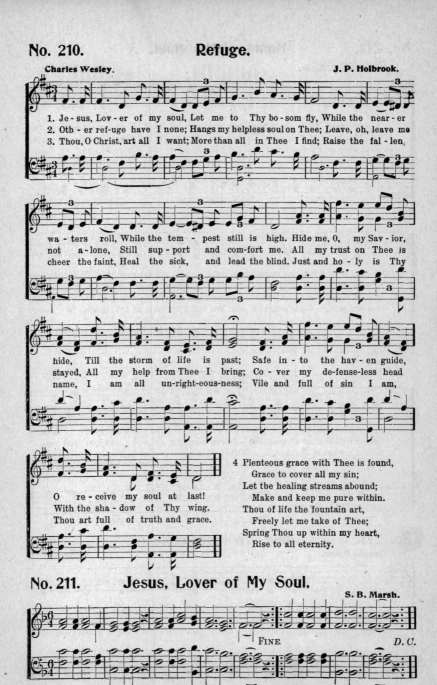

No. 210.

Charles Wesley.

Refuge.

J. P. Holbrook.

1. Je - sus, Lov - er of my soul, Let me to Thy bo - som fly, While the near - er
2. Oth - er ref - uge have I none; Hangs my helpless soul on Thee; Leave, oh, leave me
3. Thou, O Christ, art all I want; More than all in Thee I find; Raise the fal - len,

wa - ters roll, While the tem - pest still is high. Hide me, O, my Sav - ior,
not a - lone, Still sup - port and com - fort me. All my trust on Thee is
cheer the faint, Heal the sick, and lead the blind. Just and ho - ly is Thy

hide, Till the storm of life is past; Safe in - to the hav - en guide,
stayed, All my help from Thee I bring; Co - ver my de - fense-less head
name, I am all un - right-eous-ness; Vile and full of sin I am,

O re - ceive my soul at last!
With the sha - dow of Thy wing.
Thou art full of truth and grace.

4 Plenteous grace with Thee is found,
    Grace to cover all my sin;
Let the healing streams abound;
    Make and keep me pure within.
Thou of life the fountain art,
    Freely let me take of Thee;
Spring Thou up within my heart,
    Rise to all eternity.

No. 211. ## Jesus, Lover of My Soul.

S. B. Marsh.

FINE.

D. C.

No. 212. Home of the Soul.

Mrs. Ellen H. Gates.

Philip Phillips.

1. I will sing you a song of that beau-ti-ful land, The far-a-way home of the soul; Where no storms ev-er beat on the glit-tering strand, While the years of e-ter-ni-ty roll, While the years of e-ter-ni-ty roll; ty roll.

2. Oh, that home of the soul, in my vis-ions and dreams Its bright jas-per walls I can see; Till I fan-cy but thin-ly the veil in-ter-venes Be-tween the fair cit-y and me, Be-tween the fair cit-y and me; and me.

3. That unchange-a-ble home is for you and for me, Where Je-sus of Naz-a-reth stands; The King of all king-doms for-ev-er is He; And He hold-eth our crowns in His hands, And He hold-eth our crowns in His hands; His hands.

4. Oh, how sweet it will be in that beau-ti-ful land, So free from all sor-row and pain, With songs on our lips and with harps in our hands, To meet one an-oth-er a-gain, To meet one an-oth-er a-gain; a-gain.

No. 213. Come, Ye Disconsolate.

Thomas Moore.

S. Webbe.

1. Come, ye dis-con-so-late, wher-e'er ye lan-guish, Come to the
2. Joy of the des-o-late, light of the stray-ing, Hope of the
3. Here see the Bread of Life; see wa-ters flow-ing Forth from the

Come, Ye Disconsolate.

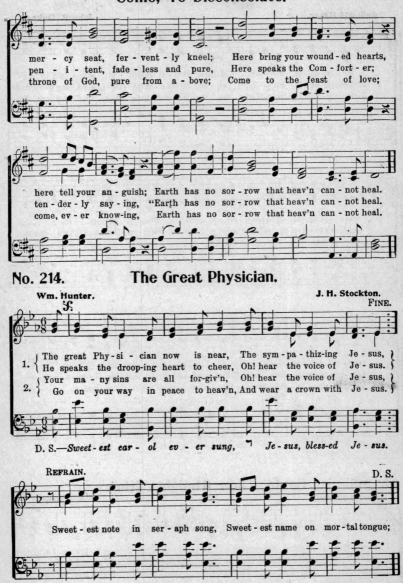

mer - cy seat, fer - vent - ly kneel; Here bring your wound - ed hearts,
pen - i - tent, fade - less and pure, Here speaks the Com - fort - er;
throne of God, pure from a - bove; Come to the feast of love;

here tell your an - guish; Earth has no sor - row that heav'n can - not heal.
ten - der - ly say - ing, "Earth has no sor - row that heav'n can - not heal.
come, ev - er know - ing, Earth has no sor - row that heav'n can - not heal.

No. 214. The Great Physician.

Wm. Hunter. J. H. Stockton.
FINE.

1. { The great Phy - si - cian now is near, The sym - pa - thiz - ing Je - sus, }
   { He speaks the droop - ing heart to cheer, Oh! hear the voice of Je - sus, }
2. { Your ma - ny sins are all for - giv'n, Oh! hear the voice of Je - sus, }
   { Go on your way in peace to heav'n, And wear a crown with Je - sus. }

D. S.—Sweet - est car - ol ev - er sung, Je - sus, bless - ed Je - sus.

REFRAIN. D. S.

Sweet - est note in ser - aph song, Sweet - est name on mor - tal tongue;

3 All glory to the dying Lamb!
  I now believe in Jesus;
  I love the blessed Savior's name,
  I love the name of Jesus.

4 His name dispels my guilt and fear,
  No other name but Jesus;
  Oh! how my soul delights to hear
  The charming name of Jesus.

Holy, Holy, Holy.

Reginald Heber.   John B. Dykes.

1. Ho-ly, ho-ly, ho-ly, Lord God Al-might-y! Ear-ly in the
2. Ho-ly, ho-ly, ho-ly! all the saints a-dore Thee, Cast-ing down their
3. Ho-ly, ho-ly, ho-ly! tho' the dark-ness hide Thee, Tho' the eye of

morn - ing our song shall rise to Thee: Ho-ly, ho-ly, ho-ly,
gold-en crowns a-round the glass-y sea; Cher-u-bim and sera-phim
sin-ful man Thy glo-ry may not see: On-ly Thou art ho-ly;

mer - ci - ful and might-y, God in Three Per-sons, bless-ed Trin-i-ty!
fall-ing down be-fore Thee, Which wert, and art, and ev-er-more shalt be.
there is none be-side Thee, Per-fect in pow'r, in love, and pu-ri-ty.

No. 216. **Come, Thou Almighty King.**

Charles Wesley.   Felice Giardini.

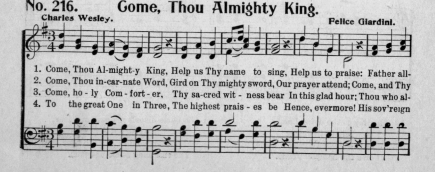

1. Come, Thou Al-might-y King, Help us Thy name to sing, Help us to praise: Father all-
2. Come, Thou in-car-nate Word, Gird on Thy mighty sword, Our prayer attend; Come, and Thy
3. Come, ho-ly Com-fort-er, Thy sa-cred wit-ness bear In this glad hour; Thou who al-
4. To the great One in Three, The highest prais-es be Hence, evermore! His sov'reign

Come Thou Almighty King.

glo - ri-ous, O'er all vic - to - ri-ous, Come and reign o - ver us, An-cient of days!
peo - ple bless, And give Thy word success: Spir-it of ho - li-ness, On us de-scend!
might-y art, Now rule in ev'ry heart, And ne'er from us de-part, Spir - it of pow'r!
maj - es - ty May we in glo-ry see, And to e - ter - ni - ty Love and a - dore!

No. 217.   Lead, Kindly Light.

J. H. Newman.   J. B. Dykes.

1. Lead, kindly Light, a - mid th' encircling gloom Lead Thou me on; The night is
2. I was not ev - er thus, nor prayed that Thou Shouldst lead me on;   I loved to
3. So long Thy pow'r has blest me, sure it still Will lead me on O'er moor and

dark, and I am far from home; Lead Thou me on: Keep Thou my feet; I
choose and see my path; but now Lead Thou me on. I loved the gar - ish
fen, o'er crag and tor-rent, till The night is gone; And with the morn those

do not ask to see The dis - tant scene,—one step e - nough for me.
day, and, spite of fears, Pride ruled my will: Re-mem-ber not past years.
an - gel-fa - ces smile, Which I have loved long since, and lost a - while.

No. 218.

Glory to His Name.

Rev. E. A. Hoffman.

Rev. J. H. Stockton.

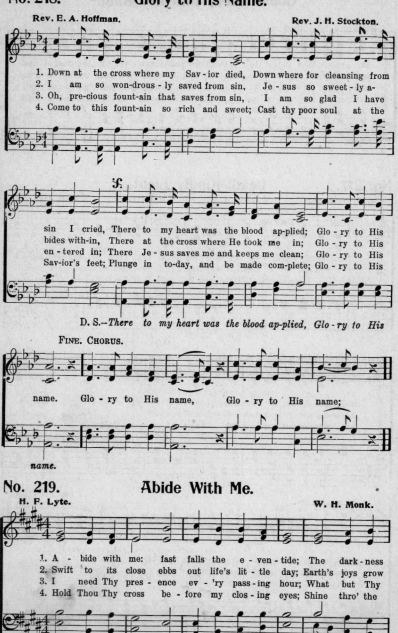

1. Down at the cross where my Sav-ior died, Down where for cleansing from
2. I am so won-drous-ly saved from sin, Je-sus so sweet-ly a-
3. Oh, pre-cious fount-ain that saves from sin, I am so glad I have
4. Come to this fount-ain so rich and sweet; Cast thy poor soul at the

sin I cried, There to my heart was the blood ap-plied; Glo-ry to His
bides with-in, There at the cross where He took me in; Glo-ry to His
en-tered in; There Je-sus saves me and keeps me clean; Glo-ry to His
Sav-ior's feet; Plunge in to-day, and be made com-plete; Glo-ry to His

D. S.—*There to my heart was the blood ap-plied, Glo-ry to His*

Fine. Chorus.

name. Glo-ry to His name, Glo-ry to His name;

name.

No. 219.

Abide With Me.

H. F. Lyte.

W. H. Monk.

1. A-bide with me: fast falls the e-ven-tide; The dark-ness
2. Swift to its close ebbs out life's lit-tle day; Earth's joys grow
3. I need Thy pres-ence ev-'ry pass-ing hour; What but Thy
4. Hold Thou Thy cross be-fore my clos-ing eyes; Shine thro' the

Abide with Me.

deep - ens; Lord, with me a - bide! When oth - er help - ers
dim, its glo - ries pass a - way; Change and de - cay in
grace can foil the tempt-er's pow'r? Who, like Thy - self, my
gloom, and point me to the skies; Heav'n's morn - ing breaks, and

fail, and com - forts flee, Help of the help - less, oh, a - bide with me!
all a - round I see; O Thou who chang - est not, a - bide with me!
guide and stay can be? Thro' cloud and sun - shine, oh, a - bide with me!
earth's vain shadows flee; In life, in death, O Lord, a - bide with me!

No. 220. Home, Sweet Home.

1. { 'Mid scenes of confusion and creature complaints } saints! To find at the banquet of
   { How sweet to my soul is com-mun - ion with }
2. { An al - ien from God, and a stran-ger to grace, } trace; In the pathway of sin I con-
   { I wandered thro' earth, its gay pleasures to }
3. { The pleas-ures of earth I have seen fade a-way; } cay; But pleasures more lasting in
   { They bloom for a sea-son, but soon they de- }

FINE. CHORUS.   D. S.

mer-cy there's room, And feel in the presence of Je-sus at home.
tin - ued to roam, Unmindful, alas! that it led me from home. Home, home, sweet, sweet home;
Je - sus are giv'n, Sal-va-tion on earth and a mansion in heav'n.

D. S.—Prepare me, dear Savior, for heaven my home.

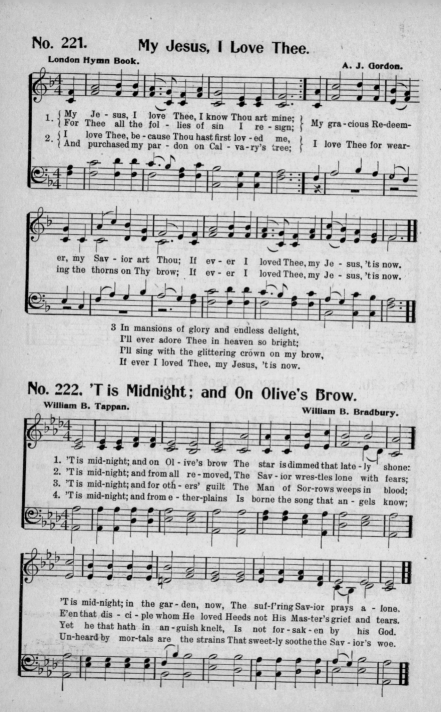

No. 221. **My Jesus, I Love Thee.**

London Hymn Book.

A. J. Gordon.

1. { My Je-sus, I love Thee, I know Thou art mine;
For Thee all the fol-lies of sin I re-sign; } My gra-cious Re-deem-

2. { I love Thee, be-cause Thou hast first lov-ed me,
And purchased my par-don on Cal-va-ry's tree; } I love Thee for wear-

er, my Sav-ior art Thou; If ev-er I loved Thee, my Je-sus, 'tis now.
ing the thorns on Thy brow; If ev-er I loved Thee, my Je-sus, 'tis now.

3 In mansions of glory and endless delight,
I'll ever adore Thee in heaven so bright;
I'll sing with the glittering crown on my brow,
If ever I loved Thee, my Jesus, 'tis now.

No. 222. **'T is Midnight; and On Olive's Brow.**

William B. Tappan.

William B. Bradbury.

1. 'T is mid-night; and on Ol-ive's brow The star is dimmed that late-ly shone;
2. 'T is mid-night; and from all re-moved, The Sav-ior wres-tles lone with fears;
3. 'T is mid-night; and for oth-ers' guilt The Man of Sor-rows weeps in blood;
4. 'T is mid-night; and from e-ther-plains Is borne the song that an-gels know;

'T is mid-night; in the gar-den, now, The suf-f'ring Sav-ior prays a-lone.
E'en that dis-ci-ple whom He loved Heeds not His Mas-ter's grief and tears.
Yet he that hath in an-guish knelt, Is not for-sak-en by his God.
Un-heard by mor-tals are the strains That sweet-ly soothe the Sav-ior's woe.

Battle Hymn of the Republic.

Julia Ward Howe. Melody, "Glory Hallelujah."

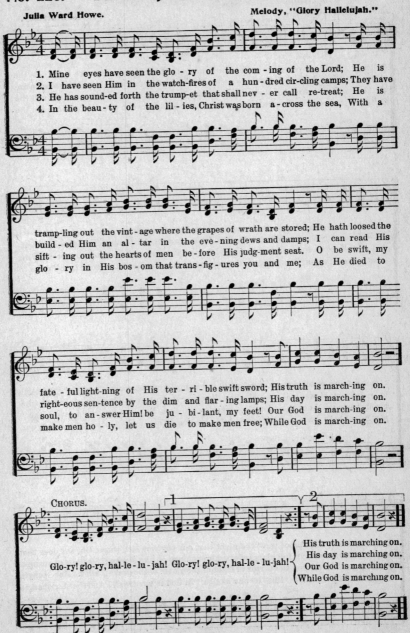

1. Mine eyes have seen the glo - ry of the com - ing of the Lord; He is
2. I have seen Him in the watch-fires of a hun - dred cir-cling camps; They have
3. He has sound-ed forth the trump-et that shall nev - er call re-treat; He is
4. In the beau-ty of the lil - ies, Christ was born a - cross the sea, With a

tramp-ling out the vint - age where the grapes of wrath are stored; He hath loosed the
build - ed Him an al - tar in the eve - ning dews and damps; I can read His
sift - ing out the hearts of men be - fore His judg-ment seat. O be swift, my
glo - ry in His bos - om that trans-fig - ures you and me; As He died to

fate - ful light-ning of His ter - ri - ble swift sword; His truth is march-ing on.
right-eous sen-tence by the dim and flar - ing lamps; His day is march-ing on.
soul, to an-swer Him! be ju - bi - lant, my feet! Our God is march-ing on.
make men ho - ly, let us die to make men free; While God is march-ing on.

CHORUS.

Glo-ry! glo-ry, hal-le - lu - jah! Glo-ry! glo-ry, hal-le - lu-jah!

His truth is marching on.
His day is marching on.
Our God is marching on.
While God is marching on.

No. 224. The Star-Spangled Banner.

Solo or Quartet.

Francis Scott Key.

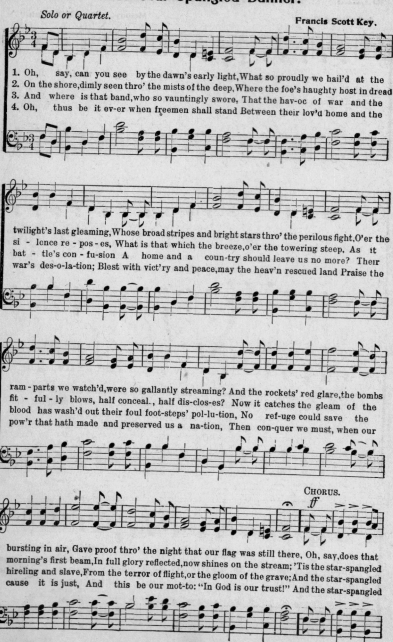

1. Oh, say, can you see by the dawn's early light, What so proudly we hail'd at the
2. On the shore, dimly seen thro' the mists of the deep, Where the foe's haughty host in dread
3. And where is that band, who so vauntingly swore, That the hav-oc of war and the
4. Oh, thus be it ev-er when freemen shall stand Between their lov'd home and the

twilight's last gleaming, Whose broad stripes and bright stars thro' the perilous fight, O'er the
si - lence re - pos - es, What is that which the breeze, o'er the towering steep, As it
bat - tle's con - fu-sion A home and a coun-try should leave us no more? Their
war's des-o-la-tion; Blest with vict'ry and peace, may the heav'n rescued land Praise the

ram - parts we watch'd, were so gallantly streaming? And the rockets' red glare, the bombs
fit - ful - ly blows, half conceal., half dis-clos-es? Now it catches the gleam of the
blood has wash'd out their foul foot-steps' pol-lu-tion, No ref-uge could save the
pow'r that hath made and preserved us a na-tion, Then con-quer we must, when our

CHORUS.

ff

bursting in air, Gave proof thro' the night that our flag was still there, Oh, say, does that
morning's first beam, In full glory reflected, now shines on the stream; 'Tis the star-spangled
hireling and slave, From the terror of flight, or the gloom of the grave; And the star-spangled
cause it is just, And this be our mot-to: "In God is our trust!" And the star-spangled

The Star-Spangled Banner.

star-spangled ban-ner yet wave O'er the land of the free, and the home of the brave?
ban-ner; oh, long may it wave O'er the land of the free, and the home of the brave?
ban-ner in tri-umph doth wave O'er the land of the free, and the home of the brave?
ban-ner in tri-umph shall wave O'er the land of the free, and the home of the brave?

No. 225. ## America.

S. F. Smith.   The National Song of America.   English.

1. My country! 'tis of thee, Sweet land of lib-er-ty, Of thee I sing; Land where my
2. My na-tive coun-try, thee, Land of the no-ble, free, Thy name I love; I love thy
3. Let music swell the breeze, And ring from all the trees Sweet freedom's song: Let mortal
4. Our father's God! to Thee, Au-thor of lib-er-ty, To Thee we sing; Long may our

fathers died, Land of the pilgrim's pride, From ev'ry mountain side, Let free-dom ring!
rocks and rills, Thy woods and templed hills; My heart with rapture thrills Like that above.
tongues awake, Let all that breathe partake, Let rocks their sil ence break, The sound prolong.
land be bright With freedom's holy light; Protect us by Thy might, Great God, our King!

No. 226. ## God Save the King.

The National Song of Britain.

1.
God save our gracious King,
Long live our noble King,
  God save the King;
Send him victorious,
Happy and glorious,
Long to reign over us,
  God save the King.

2.
Thro' every changing scene,
O Lord, preserve our King,
  Long may he reign;
His heart inspire and move
With wisdom from above,
And in a nation's love
  His throne maintain.

3.
Thy choicest gifts in store,
On him be pleased to pour,
  Long may he reign;
May he defend our laws,
And ever give us cause,
To sing with heart and voice,
  God save the King.

Responsive Readings

No. 229. The Church.

1. He saith unto them, But who say ye that I am?

2. And Simon Peter answered and said, Thou art the Christ, the Son of the living God.

3. And Jesus answered and said unto them, Blessed are thou, Simon Barjona; for flesh and blood hath not revealed it unto thee, but my Father who is in heaven.

4. And I also say unto thee, that thou art Peter, and upon this rock I will build my church; and the gates of Hades shall not prevail against it.—Matt. 16: 15-18.

5. For other foundation can no man lay than that which is laid, which is Jesus Christ.—1. Cor. 3: 11.

6. Ye are fellow citizens with the saints, and of the household of God.

7. Being built upon the foundation of the apostles and prophets, Christ Jesus himself being the chief corner stone;

8. In whom each several building, fitly framed together, groweth into a holy temple in the Lord.—Eph. 2: 19-21.

9. And he is the head of the body, the church: who is the beginning, the first born from the dead; that in all things he might have the pre-eminence.—Col. 1: 18.

10. Christ also loved the church, and gave Himself up for it.

11. That he might sanctify it, having cleansed it by the washing of water with the word.

12. That he might present the church to himself a glorious church, not having spot or wrinkle or any such thing; but that it might be holy and without blemish. —Eph. 5: 25-27.

13. And the Lord added to them (the church) day by day those that were being saved.—Acts. 2: 47.

14. Unto him be glory in the church and in Christ Jesus unto all generations for ever and ever.—Eph. 3: 21.

No. 230. Prayer.

1. *Jesus:* And he went forward a little, and fell on his face, and prayed, saying, My Father, if it be possible, let this cup pass from me: nevertheless, not as I will, but as thou wilt.—Matt. 26:39.

2. And there appeared unto him an angel from heaven, strengthening him.— Luke 22:43.

3. *Church:* Peter therefore was kept in the prison; but prayer was made earnestly of the church unto God for him.

4. And behold, and angel of the Lord stood by him, and a light shined in the cell: and he smote Peter on the side, and awoke him, saying, Arise up quickly, And his chains fell off from his hands.—Acts. 12:5-7.

5. *Apostles:* These all with one accord continued steadfastly in prayer, with the women, and Mary the mother of Jesus, and with his brethren.—Acts 1:14.

6. *Disciples:* And when they had prayed, the place was shaken wherein they were gathered together; and they were all filled with the Holy Spirit and they spake the word of God with boldness.—Acts 4:31.

7. *Paul and Silas:* But about midnight Paul and Silas were praying and singing hymns unto God, and the prisoners were listening to them;

8. And suddenly there was a great earth-quake, so that the foundations of the prison house were shaken: and immediately all the doors were opened; and every-one's bands were loosed.—Acts 16:25-6.

9. *James:* Confess your sins one to another, and pray one for another, that ye may be healed. The supplication of a righteous man availeth much in its working.

10. Elijah was a man of like passions with us, and he prayed feverently that it might not rain; and it rained not on the earth for three years and six months.

11. And he prayed again; and the heaven gave rain, and the earth brought forth her fruit.—Jas. 5:16-18.

No. 231.   Christian Union.

1. Behold, how good and how pleasant it is for brethren to dwell together in unity. —Psa. 133:1.

2. Neither for these only do I pray, but for them also that believe on me through their word;

3. That they may all be one; even as thou, Father, art in me, and I in thee, that they also may be in us: that the world may believe that thou didst send me.—Jno. 17:21-22.

4. And other sheep I have, which are not of this fold; them also I must bring, and they shall hear my voice; and they shall become one flock, one shepherd.—Jno. 20:16.

5. Now I beseech you brethren, through the name of our Lord Jesus Christ, that ye all speak the same thing, and that there be no divisions among you; but that ye be perfected together in the same mind, and in the same judgment.

6. For it hath been signified unto me concerning you, my brethren, by them which are of the household of Chloe, that there are contentions among you.

7. Not this I mean, that each one of you saith, I am of Paul; and I of Apollos; and I of Cephas; and I of Christ.

8. Is Christ divided? Was Paul crucified for you? or were you baptized in the name of Paul?—1 Cor. 10:13.

9. Only let your manner of life be worthy of the gospel of Christ: that whether I come and see you, or be absent, I may hear of your state, that ye stand fast in one spirit, with one soul striving for the faith of the gospel.—Phil. 1:27.

10. I was constrained to write unto you exhorting you to contend earnestly for the faith which was once for all delivered unto the saints.—Jude 3.

No. 232.   Communion.

1. For I received of the Lord that which also I delivered unto you, that the Lord Jesus in the night in which he was betrayed took bread;

2. And when He had given thanks, he brake it, and said, This is my body, which is for you; this do in remembrance of me.

3. In like manner also the cup, after supper, saying, This cup is the new covenant in my blood: This do, as often as ye drink, in remembrance of me.

4. For as often as ye eat this bread, and drink the cup, ye proclaim the Lord's death till he come.

5. Wherefore, whosoever shall eat the bread or drink the cup of the Lord in an unworthy manner, shall be guilty of the body and the blood of the Lord.

6. But let a man prove himself, and so let him eat of the bread, and drink of the cup.

7. For he that eateth and drinketh, eateth and drinketh judgment unto himself, if he discern not the body.

8. Wherefore my brethren, when ye come together to eat, wait one for another.

9. If any man is hungry, let him eat at home; that your coming together be not unto judgment. And the rest will I set in order whensoever I come.—1 Cor. 11: 23-34.

No. 233.   Faith.

1. How then shall they call on him in whom they have not believed? and how shall they believe in him whom they have not heard? and how shall they hear without a preacher?

2. And how shall they preach except they be sent?—Rom. 10: 14-15.

3. And he said unto them, Go ye into all the world, and preach the gospel to the whole creation.

4. He that believed and is baptized shall be saved; but he that disbelieveth shall be condemned.—Mrk. 16: 15-16.

5. And without faith it is impossible to be well pleasing unto him; for he that cometh to God must believe that he is, and that he is a rewarder of them that seek after him.—Heb. 11: 6.

6. But when they believed Philip, preaching good tidings concerning the kingdom of God and the name of Jesus Christ, they were baptized, both men and women. —Acts. 8: 12.

7. And Crispus, the ruler of the synagogue, believed in the Lord with all his house; and many of the Corinthians hearing believed, and were baptized.—Acts. 18: 8.

8. For God so loved the world, that he gave his only begotten Son, that whosoever believeth on him should not perish, but have eternal life.—Jno. 3: 16.

No. 234. Repentance.

1. I am not come to call the righteous but sinners to repentance.—Luke 5:32.

2. And that repentance and remission of sins should be preached in his name unto all the nations, beginning from Jerusalem.—Luke 24:47.

3. Then began he to upbraid the cities wherein most of his mighty works were done, because they repented not.—Matt. 11:20.

4. Except ye repent, ye shall all in like manner perish.—Luke 13:3.

5. The times of ignorance therefore God overlooked; but now he commandeth men that they should all everywhere repent.—Acts 17:30.

6 The men of Nineveh shall stand up in the judgment with this generation, and shall condemn it; for they repented at the preaching of Jonah; and behold, a greater than Jonah is here.—Luke 11:32.

7. The Lord is not slack concerning his promise, as some count slackness; but is long-suffering to you-ward, not wishing that any should perish, but that all should come to repentance.—2 Peter 3:9.

8. Now when they heard this, they were pricked in their heart, and said unto Peter and the rest of the apostles, Brethren, what shall we do?

9. And Peter said unto them, Repent ye, and be baptized every one of you in the name of Jesus Christ, unto the remission of your sins; and ye shall receive the gift of the Holy Spirit.—Acts 2:37-38.

10. I say unto you that even so there shall be joy in heaven over one sinner that repenteth, more than over ninety and nine righteous persons, who need no repentance.—Luke 15:7.

No. 235. Conversion of the Eunuch.

1. But an angel of the Lord spake unto Philip, saying, Arise, and go toward the south unto the way that goeth down from Jerusalem unto Gaza: the same is desert.

2. And he arose and went: and behold, a man of Ethiopia, a eunuch of great authority under Candace, queen of the Ethiopians, who was over all her treasure, who had come to Jerusalem to worship;

3. And he was returning and sitting in his chariot, and was reading the prophet Isaiah.

4. And the Spirit said unto Philip, Go near, and join thyself to this chariot.

5. And Philip ran to him, and heard him reading Isaiah the Prophet, and said Understandest thou what thou readest?

6. And he said, How can I, except some one shall guide me? And he besought Philip to come up and sit with him.

7. Now the passage of the scripture which he was reading was this, He was led as a sheep to the slaughter; and as a lamb before her shearers is dumb, so he openeth not his mouth:

8. In his humiliation his judgment was taken away; his generation who shall declare? For his life is taken from the earth.

9. And the eunuch answered Philip, and said, I pray thee, of whom speakest the prophet this? of himself, or of some other?

10. And Philip opened his mouth, and beginning from the Scripture, preached unto him Jesus.

11. And as they went on their way they came unto a certain water; and the eunuch said, Behold, here is water; what doeth hinder me to be baptized?

12. And he commanded the chariot to stand still: and they both went down into the water, both Philip and the eunuch; and he baptized him.

13. And when they came up out of the water, the Spirit of the Lord caught away Philip; and the eunuch saw him no more, for he went on his way rejoicing.—Acts 8:2, 6-39.

No. 236.   Jesus the Savior.

1. Thou shalt call his name Jesus; for it is he that will save his people from their sins.—Matt. 1:21.

2. And the angel said unto them, Be not afraid; for behold, I bring you good tidings of great joy, which shall be to all people:

3. For there is born to you this day in the city of David, a Saviour, who is Christ the Lord.—Luke 2:10-11.

4. But Peter and the apostles answered and said, We must obey God rather than men.

5. The God of our fathers raised up Jesus, whom ye slew, hanging him on a tree.

6. Him did God exalt with his right hand to be a Prince and a Saviour, to give repentance to Israel, and remission of sins.

7. And we are witnesses to these things; and so is the Holy Spirit, whom God hath given to them that obey him.—Acts 5:29-32.

No. 237.   The Blood of Christ.

1. If we walk in the light, and he is in the light, we have fellowship one with another, and the blood of Jesus his Son cleanseth us from all sin.—1 Jno. 1:7.

2. Wherefore Jesus also, that he might sanctify the people through his own blood, suffered without the gate.

3. Let us therefore go forth unto him without the camp, bearing his reproach. —Heb. 13:12-3.

4. Being justified freely by his grace through the redemption that is in Christ Jesus:

5. Whom God set forth to be a propitiation, through faith, by his blood.— Rom. 3:24-5.

6. Knowing that ye were redeemed, not with corruptible things, with silver or gold, from your vain manner of life, handed down from your fathers;

7. But with precious blood, as of the lamb without blemish and without spot, even the blood of Christ:

8. Who was fore-known indeed before the foundation of the world, but was manifested at the end of the time for your sake,

9. Who through him are believers in God, which raised him from the dead, and gave him glory; so that your faith and hope might be in God.—1 Pet. 1:18-21.

No. 238.   Psalm Twenty Three.

1. The Lord is my shepherd; I shall not want.

2. He maketh me to lie down in green pastures: he leadeth me beside the still waters.

3 He restoreth my soul: he leadeth me in the paths of righteousness for his name's sake.

4. Yea, though I walk through the valley of the shadow of death: I will fear no evil: for thou art with me: thy rod and thy staff they comfort me.

5. Thou preparest a table before me in the presence of mine enemies: thou anointest my head with oil; my cup runneth over.

6. Surely goodness and mercy shall follow me all the days of my life: and I will dwell in the house of the Lord forever.

No. 239.   Psalm One.

1. Blessed is the man that walketh not in the counsel of the wicked, nor standeth in the way of sinners, nor sitteth in the seat of the scoffers;

2. But his delight is in the law of Jehovah; and on his law doth he meditate day and night.

3. And he shall be like a tree planted by the streams of water, that bringeth forth its fruit in its season, whose leaf also doth not wither; and whatsoever he doeth shall prosper.

4. The wicked are not so, but are like the chaff which the wind driveth away.

5. Therefore the wicked shall not stand in the judgment, nor sinners in the congregation of the righteous.

6. For Jehovah knoweth the way of the righteous; but the way of the wicked shall perish.

No. 240.   The Holy Spirit.

1. And he, when he is come, will convict the world in respect of sin, and of righteousness, and of judgment:

2. Of sin, because they believe not on me;

3. Of righteousness, because I go to the father, and ye behold me no more;

4. Of judgment, because the Prince of this world hath been judged.—Jno. 16: 8-11.

5. Nevertheless I tell you the truth: It is expedient for you that I go away; for if I go not away, the Comforter will not come unto you; but if I go, I will send him unto you.—Jno. 16: 7.

6. But the Comforter, even the Holy Spirit, whom the Father will send in my name, he shall teach you all things, and bring to your remembrance all that I said unto you.—Jno. 14: 36.

7. But ye shall receive power, when the Holy Spirit is come upon you: and ye shall be my witnesses both in Jerusalem, and in all Judea, and Samaria and unto the uttermost part of the earth.—Acts. 1: 8.

8. Go ye therefore, and make disciples of all the nations, baptizing them into the name of the Father, and of the Son, and of the Holy Spirit:

9. Teaching them to observe all things whatsoever I commanded you: and lo, I am with you always even unto the end of the world.—Matt. 28: 19-20.

10. Jesus answered Verily, verily, I say unto thee, Except one be born of water and the Spirit, he cannot enter into the Kingdom of God. —Jno. 3: 5.

No. 241. The Conversion of the Three Thousand.

1. But ye shall receive power when the Holy Spirit is come upon you: and ye shall be my witnesses both in Jerusalem, and in all Judea, and Samaria, and unto the uttermost part of the earth.—Acts 1:8.

2. And when the day of Pentecost was now come, they were altogether in one place.

3. And suddenly there came from heaven a sound as of the rushing of a mighty wind, and it filled all the house where they were sitting.

4. And there appeared unto them tongues parting asunder, like as of fire; and it sat upon each one of them.

5. And they were all filled with the Holy Spirit, and began to speak with other tongues, as the Spirit gave them utterance.—Acts 2:1-4.

6. Now when they heard this, they were pricked in their heart, and said unto Peter and the rest of the apostles, Brethren, what shall we do?

7. And Peter said unto them, Repent ye, and be baptized everyone of you in the name of Jesus Christ for the remission of your sins; and ye shall receive the gift of the Holy Spirit.

8. For to you is the promise, and to your children, and to all that are afar-off, even as many as the Lord our God shall call unto him.

9. They then that received his word were baptized: and there were added unto them in that day about 3000 souls.—Acts 2: 37-39, 41.

No. 242.   Confessing Christ.

1. Everyone therefore who shall confess me before men, him will I also confess before my father which is in heaven.

2. But whosoever shall deny me before men, him will I also deny before my father which is in heaven.—Matt. 10:32-3.

3. Wherefore also God highly exalted him, and gave unto him the name which is above every name;

4. That in the name of Jesus every knee should bow, of things in heaven and things on earth and things under the earth,

5. And that every tongue should confess that Jesus Christ is Lord, to the glory of God the Father.—Phil. 2:9-11.

6. The word is nigh thee, in thy mouth and in thy heart; that is the word of faith, which we preach:

7. Because if thou shalt confess with thy mouth Jesus as Lord, and shalt believe in thy heart that God raised him from the dead, thou shalt be saved;

8. For with the heart man believeth unto righteousness; and with the mouth confession is made unto salvation.—Rom. 10:8-10.

No. 243. Conversion of the Jailor.

1. But about midnight Paul and Silas were praying and singing hymns unto God, and the prisoners were listening to them;

2. And suddenly there was a great earthquake, so that the foundations of the prison house was shaken: and immediately all the doors were opened; and everyone's bands were loosed.

3. And the jailer, being roused out of sleep and seeing the prison doors open, drew his sword and was about to kill himself, supposing that the prisoners had escaped.

4. But Paul cried with a loud voice, saying, Do thyself no harm: for we are all here.

5. And he called for light and sprang in, and, trembling for fear, fell down before Paul and Silas, and brought them out and said, Sirs, what must I do to be saved?

6. And they said, Believe on the Lord Jesus, and thou shalt be saved, thou and thy house.

7. And they spake the word of the Lord unto him, with all that were in his house.

8. And he took them the same hour of the night, and washed their stripes; and was baptized he and all his, immediately.

9. And he brought them up into his house and set food before them, and rejoiced greatly, with all his house, having believed in God.—Act. 16: 25-34.

No. 244. In Christ.

1. Wherefore if any man is in Christ, he is a new creature: the old things are passed away; behold, they are become new.

2. But all things are of God, who reconciled us to himself through Christ and gave unto us the ministry of reconciliation.—2 Cor. 5:17-18.

3. There is therefore now no condemnation to them that are in Christ Jesus,

4. For the law of the Spirit of life in Christ Jesus made me free from the law of sin and of death.—Rom. 8:1-2.

5. Blessed be the God and Father of our Lord Jesus Christ, who hath blessed us with ever spiritual blessing in the heavenly places in Christ.

6. Even as he chose us in him before the foundation of the world, that we should be holy and without blemish before him in love:

7. Having foreordained us unto adoption as sons through Jesus Christ unto himself, according to the good pleasures of his will,

8. In whom we have our redemption through his blood, the forgiveness of our trespasses, according to the riches of his grace.—Eph. 1:3-7.

9. If then you were raised together with Christ, seek the things that are above where Christ is, seated on the right hand of God.

10. Set your mind on the things that are above, not on the things that are upon the earth.

11. For he died, and your life is hid with Christ in God.—Col. 3:1-3.

No. 245. Wine is a Mocker.

1. Wine is a mocker, strong drink a brawler; and whosoever erreth thereby is not wise.—Prov. 20:1.

2. He that loveth pleasure shall be a poor man: he that loveth wine and oil shall not be rich.—Prov. 21:17.

3. Who hath woe? who hath sorrow? who hath contentions? who hath complainings? who hath wounds without cause? who hath redness of eyes?

4. They that tarry long at the wine; they that go to seek out mixed wine.

5. Look not thou upon the wine when it is red, when it sparkleth in the cup, when it goeth down smoothly:

6. At the last it biteth like a serpent and stingeth like an adder.—Prov. 23: 29-32.

7. And every man that striveth in the games is temperate in all things. Now they do it to receive a corruptible crown; but we an incorruptible.

8. I therefore so run, as not uncertainly; so fight I, as not beating the air:

9. But I buffet my body, and bring it into bondage: lest my any means, after that I have preached to others, I myself should be rejected.—1 Cor. 9:25-27.

10. And be not drunken with wine wherein, is riot, but be filled with the spirit.—Eph. 5:18.

Index

INDEX.

INDEX.

INDEX.

224